What Modern Hypnotism Can Do for You

What Modern Hypnotism Can Do for You

by SIDNEY PETRIE

in association with

ROBERT B. STONE

A FAWCETT CREST BOOK

Fawcett Publications, Inc., Greenwich, Conn.

To my wife, Iris, who encouraged me

To Doctors Cohn, Dunne, Engelson,
Fields, Franklin, Kemp, Neddar,
Sollinger, and Wise, who placed their
confidence in me

To my patients, who imparted knowledge to me
S.P.

WHAT MODERN HYPNOTISM CAN DO FOR YOU

THIS BOOK CONTAINS THE COMPLETE TEXT OF THE
ORIGINAL HARDCOVER EDITION.

A Fawcett Crest Book reprinted by arrangement with
Hawthorn Books.

Library of Congress Catalog Card Number: 67-24656

Printed in the United States of America
July 1972

Contents

1

From Darkness into Light

The Memorial Day parade swings up Main Street. Oompah, oompah, oompah-pah. Firemen and boy scouts move in precise rhythm. Onlookers young and old line the curb, transfixed.

A family is watching television. Action in the western drama has been temporarily halted to permit a well-known car manufacturer to point up the merits of his product. Dad, mother, and the youngsters sit patiently, relaxed.

A minister is developing his sermon. Light streams through vaulted stained-glass windows, casting blue and rose patterns on the pulpit. The congregation listens, is inspired, moved.

These three scenes may seem to have little in common. But to the scientist familiar with the workings of the human mind, there is in each a very definite element of *hypnotism*.

To many this word sounds an alarm: "I am being duped," "I am being brainwashed," "I am being mentally taken." They remember the reputed power of Svengali. They recall the curious antics of people hypnotized by a night club performer. They may even be thinking of the murder trial, the rape case, the will probate where hypnotism was the "evil tool." Their guard is up.

However, the twentieth century can claim among its vast accomplishments the emergence of hypnotism from darkness into light. It remains a tool, but a tool for the furtherance of man's skills, the elimination of his burdens, and the improvement of his health. Man today understands hypnotism enough to realize how much more he has to learn about it. Meanwhile, the knowledge that he does have permits him to surpass the fire-walking miracle maker of yesteryear and to perform a new kind of miracle.

A tooth is extracted without anesthesia and without pain. A woman gives birth without drugs and without tension. A blind person sees again. A deaf person hears again. Thousands relax and give themselves posthypnotic suggestions to substitute slenderizing eating habits for fattening ways. Other thousands seek help from hypnologists, a hypnotist who devotes his skills to clinical practice, to enable them to substitute positive attitudes for negative attitudes and release themselves from prisons of fear and self-limitation.

The parade, the television commercial, and the sermon are not hypnotically contrived devices. But they are examples of the many facets to our daily life that involve the subconscious in a significant way. *Transfixed, relaxed, moved* are the key words. They mean that our mental computer is being programmed, that the images we are receiving have a clear circuit to the storage cells of the mind, that they will be held until the proper circumstances trigger their release to motivate our thoughts and actions.

This programming of our subconscious computer is going on constantly. Sometimes it is in tiny impulses that need years to build up any real effect on our behavior. Other times, when the fixation of attention, the relaxation of the body, or the involvement of the emotions are present, the programming can be instantaneous.

The dynamics of hypnotism include attention, relaxation, and emotion. The techniques of this science of hypnotism, properly used, can change our life in whatever direction we wish it to go.

The vast reaches of the subconscious mind have taken

their place as a frontier along with the vast reaches of space. Their exploration is equally fascinating and perhaps infinitely more important to health and well-being. This book takes you on such an exploration. It discusses new frontiers that promise to shape tomorrow's world.

The Promise of Hypnotism

There is a school in St. Louis where an entire class is hypnotized and given positive suggestions to increase the students' learning motivation and receptivity. Another school in Rome, Italy, extends this to feed blocks of curriculum information right into the subconscious, circumventing hours of tedious memory work. Hypnologists are helping teachers in both public and private schools here and abroad to improve their ability to concentrate. Retarded children are gaining retention ability through hypnosis. Actors have found the hypnologist can save them hours of time in learning roles.

The information explosion poses challenges to the comprehension of the conscious mind. Yet it is quite possible that the information having to do with man's subconscious mind will itself help him solve the problem of the whole body of expanded information. Through hypnotism man is learning about learning itself.

In later chapters we will visit one of the classrooms where hypnotism is used. We will also sit in on a session where the ability to concentrate is improved. And later we will observe how an actor mentally absorbs his role as easily as blotting paper soaks up ink.

We will visit hospitals where the promise of hypnotism is one of life over death. We will watch as the hypnologist helps surgeons stop the flow of blood by command. We will listen in as a heart patient is insulated from further coronary damage that could result through his own anxiety about his condition. We will witness a hypnotic session that cured a neck condition and avoided complicated neurosurgery.

We will eavesdrop as hypnoanalysis is used to uncover emotional problems buried deep in the subconscious of men and women. We will see impotent men turn virile and frigid women thaw. We will witness the strange phenomenon of time distortion as mature adults re-enact their childhood days, their infant days and apparently even days before birth.

We will look over the hypnologist's shoulder as he induces stages of hypnosis varying from full consciousness and clear memory with total recall to deep sleeplike trance and an obedient memory with no recall. At both extremes we will see suggestions implanted in the subconscious and later enacted as though voluntary.

We will see hypnosis used by alcoholics, smokers, and bed wetters. We will see it used by athletes, politicians, and astronauts. We will see it used for the mentally retarded, the manic depressive, and the neurotic.

In short, we will see how understanding this phenomenon called hypnotism will dispel the fears and false beliefs that have surrounded the subject in a veil of taboo, and instead permit its promise to be viewed in true perspective.

It is the promise of an almost diseaseless world. It is the promise of man's mentality multiplied many times. It is the promise of greater insight into the very nature of man. It is doubtful that a trip to another planet could offer more!

Why Understand It

A woman suffering from multiple sclerosis came to a man who she had heard was knowledgeable in the field of hypnosis. He did not have a clinical practice, but he had mastered some of the techniques and had practiced them on an increasing number of persons without charge, helping them at times and simultaneously expanding his own experience.

Since the woman was under the treatment of a physician, the budding hypnotist phoned him to explain what he proposed to do for her following a test. The physician told him to proceed with the test but to write him in detail what would be involved in the subsequent treatments.

In the first hypnosis session, the woman was able to raise her arm despite weakened muscles wasted by the advanced disease. She was greatly heartened. It was the first ray of hope she had had about her condition during the months of the disease's progression. The student hypnotist wrote her physician of this first success and of his plans to exercise and strengthen the muscles during subsequent sessions.

On receipt of the letter, the physician phoned him and gave him full permission to proceed as planned. "I can see that only good can come out of this," he said. "Wonderful," said the hypnotist; "could you send me a letter of permission to that effect?" "Oh, I could not do that," replied the physician. As a result of the reservations on the part of this physician, the woman was deprived of the only known techniques that might have prolonged her physical vitality and her life.

The multiple sclerosis sufferer, her physician, and the hypnotist are among millions now caught in the circle of nonstatus. They have been immobilized by hypnotism's far too narrow band of professional acceptance. The physician knows that his colleagues have had dramatic results, but few physicians have had firsthand experience with hypnotism.

Nor are they able to obtain such experience as easily as they would with a new drug or a new surgical technique. If they want to learn the science of hypnotism, they are hard put to find a nearby center where it is taught. Medical students themselves are not offered hypnotism except occasionally as part of an elective that must take a back seat to more widely accepted medical priorities.

Meanwhile the tail has started to wag the dog. People hear about the quick successes of hypnotism. They ask their family doctors. More often than not the subject is brushed aside with a shrug or a wave of the hand. They ask their neighbors. Somebody knows somebody who was hypnotized once. The trail grows warm. It leads to an amateur, or an entertainer, or a medical man or dentist who may have sketchy knowledge. The results, often good and even often miraculous sounding, are brought back to the original physician. This becomes felt as steady public pressure. This pressure is also felt at educational levels and in the professional societies.

This public demand has led to the birth of a new type of therapist: the clinical hypnologist. He accepts referrals from physicians. He is a skilled technician and knows both the art and the science of inducing hypnosis, handling the hypnotic state, and terminating it. He has an office. He practices full time. He works closely with the physician. He knows what cases to accept and what cases to refuse. He takes thirty, forty, or fifty minutes or whatever time is necessary to complete the procedure, moving at the relaxed pace that hypnotism demands, but which today's harried physician never really knows.

He is a rare person. There are no statistics as to how many he numbers in this country. There is no school turning him out. He is synthesizing himself from the ranks of psychotherapists, psychologists, and serious-minded lay persons. As understanding of hypnotism spreads at all levels, his tribe is destined to increase.

Misunderstanding has deprived mankind of the blessings of hypnotism for more than a century. This misunderstanding began with the very naming of the hypnotic phenomenon, purportedly by an English physician, Dr. James Braid, in 1843. "Hypnosis" is a term derived from the Greek "Hypnos," God of Sleep. That was the first mistake. Hypnosis and sleep are not even cousins.

A parade of misunderstandings followed; they will unfold in the chapters ahead. Perhaps mankind cannot be blamed for hesitancy in trusting that which he cannot examine under a microscope or analyze in the laboratory. Hypnosis is a state of mind, and the mind, until now, has been a world apart from science.

Psychology and psychiatry have dared to explore the world of the mind. Their findings are spreading the light of understanding to this last frontier. The dawn of this light has now reached hypnotism. Millions who look will never forget the view.

How It Can Benefit

The inner circle is now reaping a harvest of speedy cures through hypnotism. People in the know who demand the latest and the best in the medical arts and who will not leave a curative stone unturned or avoid a last resort are often led to hypnotism.

"He has a serious heart murmur. He needs to be watched carefully." That statement, made by a conscientious pediatrician about a three-year-old boy, was traced twenty-five years later as the cause of the boy's anxiety symptoms—symptoms that caused serious chronic attacks of asthma and were threatening to bring on serious heart and lung problems. Disclosed by regression in hypnosis and confirmed by the parents, this early childhood suggestion and its debilitating effects were soon counteracted by posthypnotic suggestions that his heart was in good condition (which it now was) and need not be watched, and that he would undoubtedly enjoy his full life expectancy. This treatment was not easy to come by. In this case, it took persistence to find a physician able and willing to proceed with hypnotism.

Many people with a history of abdominal operations who have ended their hospital incursions with a few excursions to the land of hypnorelaxation have been fortunate. Ulcers, colitis, nausea, bloating, vomiting, diarrhea, and constipation have all disappeared quickly and permanently via hypnotism, once a practicing hypnologist could be found. What are the physical changes that a few spoken words can induce? Where can you find the man to speak them? The answers are now finding their way into medical journals and filtering out to practitioners and the public. But the pace is slow.

More frequently we hear of massive relief in cases of arthritis, rheumatism, migraine headaches, and other painful conditions. We hear the need for insulin reduced in diabetics; epileptic seizures stopped in their tracks.

Perhaps of even more significance to the healthier majority is hypnotism's ability to block pain. Women are finding it a boon for menstrual pain and childbirth. Dentists find that most patients are good patients following hypnotic suggestion and even oral surgery can be performed in many cases without the use of anesthesia. Persons suffering recurring pain of any sort can be given a suggestion while in hypnosis that when they touch the painful area with their hand the pain will ease. And so it does. One such suggestion sometimes lasts for months.

Clinical hypnosis is enjoying a surge of popularity, but the initiative is coming from the people, and their growing interest and need is hard put to find satisfaction. However, a great many physicians would like to recommend hypnosis if they knew where to refer their patients.

As a result of this shortage, self-hypnosis is being practiced as a substitute. It is being taught in special courses and through books, and is being used successfully for obesity, smoking, drug addiction, stammering, bed-wetting, thumb sucking, alcoholism, and many other areas of habit control. It is turning introverts into extroverts, laggards into go-getters, and weaklings into spellbinders.

With all this, America may still be taking a back seat to the rest of the world. Hypnotism began in Europe and its practitioners there are more numerous if not more skillful. The Russians are known to have been devoting a great deal of clinical study to the subject. In Japan, business and industry have taken the play away from the medical world by using hypnosis clinics to train salesmen, energize executives, and increase office worker efficiency.

It is not uncommon to see well-dressed Japanese businessmen gazing at a twirling device as the droning voice of a moonlighting psychology professor suggests that their minds are being purified of anxiety and distraction. One Osaka insurance company requires hypnotic training sessions for all of its salesmen. These inspirational lectures improve the personality and increase self-confidence. Although one such company in New York has adopted hypnotism, it is definitely the exception rather than the rule.

Tokyo public schools are also using hypnosis. One district school official is a self-taught hypnotist. He relaxes the class by leading them down an imaginary stairway. "When you reach the last step you can memorize more easily." The students, in both elementary and secondary grades, are enthusiastic and invariably cooperate, claiming that their work is being cut immeasurably.

In the United States, neither industries and commercial organizations, nor the schools and colleges, are following the Japanese example. When a seminar *is* held it is usually superficial and with obvious reservations. A recent three-day hypnosis workshop, aimed at developing skills among medical men, allowed more time for coffee breaks than for actual induction techniques. Only fifteen minutes of the three days' curriculum was devoted to the induction part of the technique of hypnosis. The following day, twenty minutes was scheduled for the awarding of certificates!

In the chapters ahead, the reader will discover what it feels like to be hypnotized and also what it is like to hypnotize a subject. There will be more technique described than is presented in many so-called courses. This information is necessary to have a full understanding of hypnotism, what it is, and how it works. It is not intended as a course in the practice of hypnotism. The reading of it will not qualify anyone to attempt hypnosis on himself or on others, any more than reading a book on the miracles of surgery entitles one to attempt surgery.

How It Can Harm

A stage hypnotist in Tennessee was demonstrating at a school assembly. "It's cold out and snowing," he said to his sixth grade subjects. They shivered and moved about to keep warm. "Now, it's hot. It's one hundred degrees." The shivering stopped. Collars were loosened, sweaters came off. "Watch out, there's a snake." They jumped up on chairs, except for one girl who stood as if paralyzed. Then she began to scream. The hypnotist ended the session. The youngsters rubbed their eyes, but the little girl kept screaming. She ran off the stage and down the corridor. Her hysterics increased. She was hospitalized. It took two weeks of intensive psychiatric care to end the trauma.

Hypnotherapists can be trained to detect the presence of psychoses that make hypnosis dangerous. The stage hypnotist is often too carried away with his own importance to consider the dignity or the mental health of the subject.

One professional entertainer recently said in a press interview prior to an hour's audience participation show in a "Go Go Revue" that his ground rules were that a subject must be willing to be hypnotized, must listen and do exactly what he is told, and must be relaxed. "Then the fun begins," he said. Fun, but . . .

The skilled clinical hypnologist cringes at this statement. He knows that an understanding of the patient must be acquired from the patient's physician and through direct interviews. He realizes that there are dangers in managing a subject in a state of hypnosis and he knows the precautions that must be taken. He takes those precautions. He tests, suggests, and tests again. He goes one small step at a time, always gently, always testing permission. Can a professional entertainer, intent on producing a fast-moving show, pay any mind to such vital factors? There are qualified stage hypnotists who have the sensibility to avoid error, but they are few.

Science does not know what gravity is, or electricity, or

light. Even the atom, which has given up secret after secret, retains many more. Yet science can use their energies and forces to serve man. Science does not yet know what hypnotism is, but science knows enough about its effects to place hypnotism in its proper place within the entire body of knowledge about the human mind and to make use of these effects.

As people can be injured by electricity improperly used, they can be injured by hypnotism. The same is true of self-hypnotism. Some persons have been known to use it to satisfy their inclination to fantasy formation and to get further and further from the real world. An incipient psychotic state can then become acute. A person properly trained in self-hypnosis knows that each session has a well-defined purpose and a well-defined beginning and end. Anything less can turn out to be equal to a refillable prescription for a habit-forming drug.

The skilled hypnotist or self-hypnotist knows the limitations of hypnotism and knows he dare not use it to impede the physical capacity of the person or to interfere with natural functions. What will happen if the suggestion is given that a person will find slenderizing meat and salad delicious, but fattening bread and potatoes distasteful? The person will, of course, find it more to his liking to make a meal of filet mignon and salad and skip the starch. On the other hand, what will happen if the suggestion is given that the patient will have neither hunger nor appetite? Will the person eat less? The answer is a decisive no, and where this type of suggestion has been given, the operator has often found himself with a subject who has entered the throes of deep conflict, manifested by depression, nausea, or other symptoms. These symptoms will persist until the suggestion is countermanded or reversed. In other subjects, the appetite will be dulled without apparent conflict—and even more serious injury caused by eventual malnutrition.

Qualified hypnologists recognize that the physical limitations of the body must be observed despite the apparent ability of a hypnotized person to exceed these limits. Almost everybody who has seen hypnosis in action has seen a hypnotized person lying with his head on one chair, his heels on another, and his rigid body forming a bridge between the two. Fully conscious it is a nearly impossible feat except for an acrobat. It is true that the body can perform superhuman feats under the influence of hypnotic suggestion, but there may be a price to pay in internal damage.

During the author's early days of practice, he prepared a woman patient for a tooth extraction without anesthesia. She was a good subject. The posthypnotic suggestion was given to numb the gums in the area of the extraction. The oral surgery came off without incident. Some weeks later, by coincidence, the author met the woman in a restaurant. He stopped at her table to say hello. She was eating ice cream. "You know," she said, "I can eat ice cream on that side of my mouth without any trouble." Struck with the realization of what could have happened, he asked her to touch her gums with her finger. Any feeling? "No." Sure enough, he had completely forgotten to give her a posthypnotic suggestion that would restore feeling in the gums the day after the operation. What followed was probably the first case of clinical hypnotism in a restaurant.

In the late 1950s, athletes appeared to have discovered how hypnosis could extend their physical prowess. The hundred-yard dash could be executed a half a second or more faster, and milers could chop upwards of five seconds off their best times. Shot putters gained yards, jumpers inches, and one pole vaulter bettered his own record by six inches under hypnosis. Entire teams, including the St. Louis Browns, college basketball teams, and football squads experimented with hypnosis. However, a number of cases of harmful exhaustion and muscular strain resulted because they had not observed proper preparation of the hypnotic suggestions. A joint statement on the use of hypnosis in athletics was issued in July 1960 by the Committee on the Medical Aspects of Sports and the Council on Mental Health of the American Medical Association, in which the practice of going beyond the limits of physical ability via hypnotism was sharply condemned.

Another factor that the skilled clinical hypnologist watches for is the presence of an underlying psychopathology. Oftentimes a symptom, such as overeating, will subside quickly and safely because the emotional causes that brought about the persisting habit are no longer present. On the other hand, if these causes are still present, they may manifest themselves through different symptoms if the original symptom is removed through hypnotism. This happens more rarely than is generally believed, but it deserves mention.

A classic example of this in medical annals is the woman who was cured of chain smoking and took up eating abnormal amounts. When this was treated, she turned to alcohol. If psychiatry had not then come to the rescue, it could have been drugs or suicide. Legend too is the case of the man who ground his teeth at night. His dentist used hypnotic suggestion to put a stop to it and that night the man nearly strangled his wife in his sleep. Needless to say, the dentist had to restore the teeth-grinding habit via the same hypnotic techniques.

A nineteen-year-old girl was referred to the author because she was suffering from extreme menstrual cramps. She was taught self-hypnotism to be used for relaxation to alleviate the pain. She decided on her own to use this technique to delay her menstrual period. The result was that she upset her whole glandular cycle and caused irregular periods. When she returned to her physician and was re-referred for hypnosis, her condition was returned to normal through hypnotic suggestion.

Another case of misuse resulted when a student used this skill of self-hypnotism to prolong his waking periods. He began to suffer serious headaches and attacks of fatigue. He learned quickly to give up the practice. These cases are rare.

Can I be hypnotized against my will? Would I perform an immoral act? These are the two questions that people ask most frequently. Yes and no, to both questions, are the answers they keep getting. Here is why: Hypnotism requires that the subject not resist. If the subject does resist, he or she probably cannot be hypnotized. However, a person can be hypnotized without wanting to be hypnotized; there is no consent, but neither is there opposition.

People in the audience when a stage hypnotist performs have been known to be affected. The British Broadcasting System will not televise programs showing persons hypnotized because it found that the audience developed hypnotic trance states. The author once permitted a woman's sister and friend to observe her first hypnosis session. The subject seemed to resist the eye closure suggestions, but the two witnesses went right into a fine trance state!

As to the second question regarding immoral acts under hypnosis, the answer is yes and no because it depends on just how deep the level of morality resides. If a person could be talked into an immoral act by someone with a good line, it could also happen under hypnosis, and perhaps faster and easier. But if there was not a chance of so doing, even at an intimate bar, it could not happen under hypnosis either.

Hypnotism is a valuable tool for human betterment. It can harm if used unwisely. But it can perform miracles in the attainment of health and self-mastery. Even aspirin can be dangerous if used unwisely. No one would consider consuming a whole bottle of it. And no one should consider hypnotism as a plaything. Nor should he be part of any activity where it is used by other than a properly trained operation.

A Visit to the Hypnologist

The time is today. The place is the author's office. Mrs. Jones, a forty-year-old housewife, is seated in a comfortable chair. She has been referred by her physician for assistance in weight control. We have talked about her health problems, her home and family, and her attitudes toward food and weight. We have tested her susceptibility to hypnosis and decided on a method of induction. We have agreed on a program to shift her eating habits away from sweets and starches toward the protein foods. She has agreed to relinquish some of her favorites: chocolate, cake, ice cream, bread, potatoes, spaghetti. She knows that this first hypnosis session will back up this decision with suggestions that will reach her subconscious and lessen the need for conscious exercise of will power. Temptation to eat fattening carbohydrates will subside; attraction toward appetizing meats, fish, poultry, cheese, and salads will increase.

Hypnologist: Are you comfortable? Here, take this pillow and put it behind your back. Is that better?

Mrs. Jones: Yes, that's fine.

Hypnologist: Perhaps you would like to take your hands off the the arms of the chair and place them on your lap instead.

Mrs. Jones: All right.

Hypnologist: Does that feel perfectly comfortable?

Mrs. Jones: Yes, it feels quite natural.

(The reason for all this attention to comfort is that any discomfort acts the same as distraction. It would interfere with the subject's focusing attention on the hypnologist's suggestions.)

Hypnologist: Now I want you to understand that all you have to do is relax and let my words lead your imagination from thought to thought.

(Note how the subject is put at ease. The subject is now encouraged to listen with her visual imagination as well as with her ears.)

Hypnologist: Now, Mrs. Jones, look at that light on the wall in front of you. Try not to move your eyes. If they do move, bring them back.

(There is slight authority in his voice now. He is watching her eyes. If they moisten, he will know they are about to close.)

Hypnologist: Your eyes are flickering. They are half closed. Let them close gently if you wish, but don't apply tension.

(They're playing a game with each other now. She doesn't want him to think she's hypnotized, because she knows she's not. Whereas he doesn't want to make her think she's closing her eyes because he wants her to; he'd prefer her to close them of her own volition. Look, she just lost the game.)

Hypnologist: Now let your body become very loose and and limp. Breathe deeply, exhale slowly. Concentrate your mind on your feet. They feel very heavy. You can feel the weight

of your shoes. The heaviness is spreading
to your ankles, your legs, and to your waist.

(If you are wondering why several minutes are spent in
getting across the feeling of heaviness, it is because it
brings the mind away from its normal wakened state and
permits it to slip into a never-never land that goes with a
lethargic body. You can see that Mrs. Jones is showing
signs of being thoroughly relaxed. Her head is bent
slightly forward. Her breathing is slow and regular. The
hypnologist knows just what she is feeling.)

Hypnologist: Mrs. Jones, you don't feel like moving.
                You don't feel like talking. You feel won-
                derfully relaxed and able to pay full atten-
                tion to my voice. Now imagine you are in
                an elevator high up in a building. It is safe
                and comfortable. You are at the twentieth
                floor. The elevator starts to descend slowly.
                As it goes down, you sink into an even
                more relaxed state. Each floor is numbered.
                With each passing floor you sink deeper
                and deeper. You are getting more and more
                relaxed—seventeen, sixteen, fifteen . . .

(The hypnologist is using the countdown system. He
times the count with each breath she takes. Listen, they're
arriving at the ground floor.)

Hypnologist: . . . two, one. You are now in a very deep,
                deep state of enjoyable relaxation. You can
                hear and understand everything I am about
                to tell you. I want you to picture yourself
                several months from now. You have lost
                all that excess weight you decided to lose.
                You are standing, you are wearing a white
                dress. There is a full-length mirror by you.
                It has two side mirrors so you can see
                yourself side view and front view. You look
                wonderful and feel wonderful. You ap-
                pear to be years younger, vibrant and radi-
                ant. Can you picture yourself? Raise the
                index finger of your left hand as soon as
                you can see yourself.

(Mrs. Jones responds immediately. The hypnologist picks up a piece of paper from his desk.)

Hypnologist: Here is how you will attain this image of yourself and make it come true. You will not crave or desire any of the foods that we have agreed you will not eat. You will feel thoroughly satisfied and delighted with nourishing foods that we have agreed you will eat. I have the list of food in front of me. It is the list you and I prepared. The food that you agreed not to eat is listed under "Stop" foods. The foods that you agreed were right for you are listed as "Go" foods. You will eat the "Go" foods and have no desire for the "Stop" foods. You will do this comfortably and easily, without tension or strain.

(The hypnologist devotes several minutes to these suggestions, saying the same thing in different ways. Note that he has not made any suggestion that the subject has not agreed to before. The list he holds is one they developed together. He is about to end the session.)

Hypnologist: Sit for a minute more, enjoy this feeling of relaxation. Think of yourself two months from now, slender and beautiful. Now when I count to five, this session will be over. You will feel wonderful, motivated and strong. One, two, three, four, five.

Ex-Handmaiden of Mysticism

It is hard to believe that as recently as two centuries ago hypnotism was the exclusive property of witch doctors, Greek oracles, Persian Magi, and Hindu fakirs. Miraculous healings by priests who induced sleeplike trances with ceremonial rites are recorded in early Greek medical records. Ancient Jewish cabalistic concepts had autohypnotic aspects. Indian yogis still use postures and mental exercises that border on hypnotism.

From the realm of mysticism to the modern hypnologist's office has been a tortuous trial for hypnotism. Its proponents exploited it in ways that became perfect fodder for its opponents. It developed an image of quackery rather than professionalism. The next chapter will trace these fascinating beginnings, tell how Mesmer and Coué became household names and how hypnotism's decline was so precipitous that it has fallen decades behind its proper place in medical annals.

Today the controversy over hypnotism still rages. However, now it is not over acceptance, but over who should teach it and who should use it. It is a fight over who should exercise domain over the science of hypnotism. The American Medical Association's Council on Mental Health has formed a Committee on Hypnosis. It is composed mostly of psychiatrists. It has recommended that only psychiatrists are qualified to practice hypnosis. Psychologists have moved faster, however. They have sponsored training institutes in hypnosis, published papers on it, and adopted hypnotism into their individual practices more universally.

The controversy spills over into legislatures almost every year, when one or more states consider laws to regulate the practice of hypnotism. No such laws have yet been passed. Perhaps this is because hypnotism is still not fully understood and perhaps it is because hypnotism is suggestion, and suggestion is as commonplace as a television commercial, a sermon, and a parade.

2

The Hypnotized State

"I wasn't really hypnotized. I was just going along with you."

"I heard everything that went on. I couldn't have been hypnotized."

"I was thinking about some shopping and errands I have to do."

These are statements made by three excellent subjects following successful hypnosis sessions. About ninety percent of those who experience the state of hypnosis deny that it has occurred. They say they feel no loss of memory, no lessening of time consciousness, no dulling of sensory awareness. Yet they do not remember what they are told not to remember. They think that the session lasted ten minutes when it was actually twenty-five minutes. And a pin may still be tucked in the skin of their finger unobserved and unfelt.

What does hypnotism look like to the subject? Like any other minute of the day, according to most subjects. They hear no strange sounds, see no hazy mists, experience no sleeplike dreams. It is usually a very unexciting experience.

What does it look like to the hypnotist of these same subjects? An entirely different story. He sees changes occur in the subject's expression. A placid look sets in. The subject does not swallow. There are no voluntary motions, such as the usual shifting in the chair, crossing of the legs, talking with the hands. If a fly walks across the forehead, there is no furrowing of the brow. He may also notice that as the lashes flicker and the eyes close, they turn upward.

There is no doubt in the mind of the hypnologist when the mind of the subject is bared to the power of suggestion. "You will feel more comfortable as your head rests on your left shoulder." The head tilts to this position. "Raise your right arm." The arm moves up in slow motion. "Now put it back down." It drops slowly. The hypnologist lifts the arm. It feels light as a feather and it stays in whatever position it is placed, or it may drop like a wet rag.

"Straighten your head. Raise both your arms and hold them straight in front of you. Now you can feel your right hand getting heavier than your left." The right hand drifts four or five inches below the left. "Are your two arms at the same level?" The subject replies in the affirmative.

Nobody can explain the hypnotized state scientifically or completely. It is believed to be part of our natural behavior, one in which the hypnotized person's consciousness narrows as it might do in daydreaming or in a trance or even in watching movies or television. Hypnotized persons are not sleeping persons. They can talk, walk, read, and write. Even under deep hypnosis, when complete anesthesia and loss of sensation results, the person can open his eyes, walk about, and carry out instructions involving simple activities. These activities do not interfere with the trance, and even a prolonged surgical operation will not disturb the hypnotic state.

Strange physical phenomena can occur in the state of hypnosis. Tell the subject that you are pressing a red hot iron to his skin and when you touch him with the cold tip of a screwdriver, a blister will form. Tell him you are touching him with cold metal, and even a red-hot soldering iron might not blister his skin. These same reversals

will occur as a posthypnotic suggestion long after the
state of hypnosis has been ended. If anyone has any doubt
about the effect of the mind over the body, the simple
demonstration of an effect such as this is strong argu-
ment.

Strange mental phenomena can occur in the state of
hypnosis. Time can be telescoped and the subject can
recall the slightest detail of his life at any age. He can
relive incidents in his past and can even feel that he
lived another life centuries before or even in prehistoric
time. He can relate all of this "recall" in a vivid, realistic
way with his voice, vocabulary, and articulation changing and becoming appropriate to the occasion. A forty-
year-old man describes his second year of life in baby
talk. A twenty-two-year-old teacher describes what she
calls a "previous life" in Shakespearean tongue. (More
about this fascinating case history, reminiscent of "Bridey
Murphy," in a future chapter.)

These strange physical and mental phenomena become
useful tools for physical and mental therapy to the skilled
clinical hypnologist. But learning how to use these as
tools did not occur overnight. For most of man's history,
these phenomena have been abused more than used. Let
us telescope time ourselves to trace its progress from the
"temple sleep" of ancient Egypt to the "computer reprogramming" of modern hypnotism.

The First Hypnotists

Scientists have observed a power, similar to hypnotism,
used by snakes. Certain species of snakes have the ability
to fix their eyes on a bird or other prey. The bird appears to be fascinated and to lose its will or ability to
escape. As it flutters helplessly, the snake approaches
for its dinner. Even a full-grown rabbit can faint under
the gaze of the serpent, who might well be called the first
hypnotist.

In 1773 Frederick Anton Mesmer presented his thesis
on "The Influence of the Stars and Planets as Curative
Powers" to the medical faculty of the University of
Vienna. The moon, sun, and stars, he said, affected humans through an invisible force he called "animal magnetism." He claimed that this force could be derived from
a magnet.

At that time a Father Hell, a Jesuit priest, was gaining fame in Vienna for obtaining cures by applying magnetized steel plates to the body. Mesmer collaborated for a while with Father Hell, but then he began to use other magnetized objects. Soon the journals were publishing stirring accounts of how apparently hopeless cases were being cured by Mesmer's magnets.

Mesmerism became a byword throughout Europe. Thousands of invalids poured into Vienna weekly for his cures. He began to use mass-production methods. Thirty or more persons would be treated at one time by grasping iron rods connected to a large tub of iron filings. Mesmer would touch each person with a glass rod, transferring from himself to the patient the magnetism that he claimed he received from astral bodies.

If we regress in time even further, we find that Mesmer was not original, but was actually following a footpath trod by scores of metaphysicians over the centuries. They included Paracelsus, Gracian, Helmont, and Maxwell. They all based their curative activities on the power of the magnet. Mesmer revived their work and accented two important ingredients: belief and expectation. When a person believed what he heard about mesmerism, he expected a cure. Where suggestion could cure, it did. Mesmer dramatized, performed, and publicized at every turn. He apparently understood the power of suggestion, but not at the expense of his belief in the power of the magnet.

Mesmer's magnetic spa became a showplace for sensationalism and eighteenth-century beatniks. His colleagues strove constantly to discredit him. Their wrath eventually forced Mesmer to flee from Vienna to Paris. Years later he returned to Vienna to die a pauper. The memoirs that survived him were those of sensationalism and quackery rather than of cure. Mesmer had trod close to the science of hypnotism, but his unprofessional reputation increased the distance between mankind and that elusive science.

It is natural that those who later dared to look with a professional eye on the undeniable effects of mesmerism and hypnotism did so with the utmost of caution and conservatism. One of Mesmer's former students, the influential Marquis de Puységur, revived the experimental activity that had all but subsided. It was, in the course of one of his experiments that he observed a curious phenomenon. A young man who was suffering from a serious lung condition with excruciating pains in the thorax and lumbar regions, was being given the magnetization treatment. He fell into what appeared to be a light sleep. De Puységur spoke to the patient of peace and relaxation. He suggested that the pain was ending and that he would experience peace, peace, peace. The patient responded instantly. The pain vanished.

Further experiments with this same man revealed even more remarkable characteristics of this trancelike state. De Puységur found that this patient spoke like an oracle while in a trance. He could tell what other people were thinking, what was going on in the next room, and even prescribed the treatment necessary for his own cure. Here were the first inklings of phenomena connected with hypnotism which would continue to puzzle scientists to the present day, and that we will discuss later.

De Puységur resisted the temptation to exploit his findings. Where Mesmer sought the spectacular, he shunned it. Yet the very fact that he dared to merge such phenomena as thought transference and clairvoyance with medical hypnotism once again drew the medical world into organized resistance.

The Hypnotized State Is Recognized

In 1815 a man by the name of Abbe Faria came to Paris from India and gave public exhibitions of the mass induction of the trancelike state. Cures were effected, but, said Faria, they were not due to magnetism, but rather to the expectancy of the person himself.

This was the beginning of a new era for hypnotism. It was sparked by knowledge from India where fakirs had been demonstrating the painkilling properties of self-induced trance for centuries and where gurus had been teaching the properties of consciousness that made it possible.

It was not long before hypnoanesthesia was tried and found successful. In 1829 Cloquet used it to perform a breast amputation before the French Academy of Medicine. At about the same time, it was introduced in the United States by Wheeler, who removed nasal polyps.

Both men called this hypnoanesthesia by the name of mesmerism.

Painless surgery attracted more and more support. James Braid, a Scottish physician, depersonalized the phenomenon by abandoning the term mesmerism, renaming it to describe its effect rather than its most flamboyant practitioner. He coined the words hypnotism and hypnosis, based on the Greek word for sleep.

Some authorities bestow the title of "Father of Modern Hypnotism" on Braid, not so much because of his naming the infant science but for his recognition of its true nature. Braid scoffed at the mysterious and occult and branded as false the "magnetic fluid" of Mesmer. Emphasizing clinical observation and the scientific method, he verified that it was primarily the degree of expectation that increased a subject's susceptibility to suggestion.

The state of hypnotism was officially recognized by the medical profession increasingly from then on. However, increase has been at such a slow rate that over a century later it still has many fields to conquer.

With its medical recognition also came recognition in religious circles. This was accelerated by Father Gassner, a Jesuit priest, who achieved no small notoriety through his use of seance-like rituals. He would enter his dimly lit, black-draped room, outstretched arms bearing a diamond-studded crucifix. His thunderous voice would then banish "evil spirits" as his piercing eyes focused on the sufferers.

A physician of the local town where Father Gassner demonstrated the curative powers of hypnosis recorded an experiment in which the subject was told her pulse was slowing.[1] The physician took the girl's pulse and confirmed the slower rate. Father Gassner suggested that the pulse would accelerate. The physician recorded a rise of fifty beats per minute.

Then the physician tells of a strange demonstration. Father Gassner told the girl to lie quietly as her pulse beat slower and slower and finally ceased. Her muscles would relax fully and she would, in effect, die momentarily, but that she should not fear for he would restore her to life, healthier than ever. The physician knelt beside her, recording her pulse as it beat slower and slower.

[1] New Concepts of Hypnosis by Bernard Gindes, M.D., Julian Press, New York, 1951.

Suddenly his face turned ashen as he arose and pronounced her dead. Gassner then commanded the heart
to beat once more. He ordered her to awake, alert and
healed. The physician felt the pulse begin. Her muscles
moved spasmodically. Then she sat up. She was entirely
normal and cured of her pains.

Eight thousand miles away, on an average day in India,
a fakir would hardly be noticed as he drew himself into
an improvised coffin and was buried by colleagues for a
brief period of self-induced, simulated death. Echoes of
the past and shadows from India have met in today's
modern hospital, where physicians have been able to
induce a very temporary suspension of heart activity
through suggestion in hypnosis.

The Hypnotized State Today

Scientific progress over the past century has been built
by such names as Freud and Coué ("Every day in every
way I am getting better and better") and recorded in
hundreds of published papers, pamphlets, and books.

Gradually the hypnotized state has become recognized
in all its many stages, and its characteristics have been
identified. Slowly, very slowly, but surely, it has become
less and less the land of dragons to its explorers and
more and more a charted land with mountains of opportunity and valleys of danger. Today medical science has
its first usable maps of the hypnotized state, though this
state still remains as a hinterland of the mind—a sort of
science where we can only speculate as to what may be
beyond.

Early hypnologists who used hypnosis for painless
surgery did not dream that their subjects were in fairly
light stages of hypnosis and that much deeper hypnosis
was possible. Today, as many as fifty stages of hypnosis
have been identified. Scales have been established and
tests developed to determine how far along that scale a
hypnotized subject has progressed.

There is no better way to clear up the many conflicting
notions about hypnotism than to observe this scale. The
budding musician begins his study of music with the do,
re, mi's; and the budding artist first learns the chromatic
scale of blues, reds, yellows, and in betweens.

The degree or depth of hypnosis cannot be measured

by an electronic meter or any other gauge. Until such a device is developed, our measuring is limited to the effects of suggestion, for suggestion is as successful as the hypnotic state is deep.

Two scales, based on these suggestions and responses, are popularly used. One is the Davis-Husband scale of hypnotic susceptibility.[2] It has thirty stages, beginning with the subject's relaxation, fluttering of the eyelids, closing of the eyes, and complete physical relaxation.

Stage numbers six through ten on this scale indicate catalepsy, the almost rigid maintenance of the physical posture. Number six is catalepsy of the eyes while number ten is full body rigidity. For many social hypnotists, this is the crowning glory. The subject can be placed in a dramatic position with no support between head and heels.

Stage eleven marks the beginning of the effects of anesthesia. It can be developed first in the hand, then in other parts of the body. By stage fifteen hypnosis is deep enough to give the subject a suggestion that will produce anesthesia in a given area hours or even days after the session has ended. This is being used quite often in dental surgery today, where the patient is prepared by the hypnologist with the suggestion that when the surgeon says "Relax," no pain will be felt in the gums.

By stage seventeen, the subject is susceptible to suggestions that can change his personality traits. Fears and phobias can be dissolved along with the self-limiting effects of suggestions recorded in his formative years.

As the stages deepen the subject becomes susceptible to all types of posthypnotic suggestions, delusions, and even complete amnesia. At stage twenty-two he can open his eyes without affecting the trance state. The final stages are a complete somnambulism when he can walk, read, write, and act on command, display physical and emotional responses to positive and negative suggestions, and hallucinate both visually and auditorially.

All of these stages are viewable by the hypnologist, but if you are the subject, you experience very little change going from one stage to another, and then only for the first five to ten stages. Your conscious awareness

[2] L. S. Davis and R. W. Husband, "A Study of Hypnotic Susceptibility in Relation to Personality Traits," *Journal of Abnormal Social Psychology*, No. 26, 1931.

has receded by that time to the point where you are a basically subconscious person.

The hypnologist, however, sees many nuances and it was Leslie M. Le Cron, working with J. Bordeaux,[3] who developed an expansion of this scale to fifty stages to more adequately reflect these nuances. For instance, it was noted that following initial glove anesthesia, a state of numbness where pressure is felt but very little pain, it was possible to create sensory illusions. You could convince a subject that ants were crawling on him, that a seat was hot, that tobacco smoke was as acrid as burning rubber, and that cake tasted like castor oil. These tactile, gustatory, and olfactory illusions are steps twenty-three to twenty-five in the Le Cron scale.

A lag in muscular reactions was detected and became stage thirty-eight. Control of the heartbeat, blood pressure, digestion, and other organic bodily functions begin at stage forty. Next comes hyperamnesia or the recall of lost memories, followed by age regression with total memory recall. At stage forty-seven dreams can be stimulated right there in the trance state or later by posthypnotic suggestion in natural sleep.

This phenomenon has long existed, but it has only recently been organized and labeled. To name something is the first step in its control, and control is a necessary part of the scientific process.

It is quite likely that these scales will one day bow to a more direct measurement of the state of hypnosis. If we were to measure electricity this way, we would say there were fifty stages of brightness in a bulb and we would devise ways of measuring that brightness perhaps from no visual brightness to near blinding brightness. Of course, we have ampere meters that register the actual flow of electric current rather than one of the effects of that flow. In the future we may find a way to scientifically measure the depth of trance or the thinness of residual consciousness as the true indicators of the state of hypnosis.

[3] L. M. Le Cron and J. Bordeaux, *Hypnotism Today*, Grune & Stratton, Inc., New York, 1947.

Who Can Be Hypnotized

Everybody can be hypnotized. This statement is true provided you are willing to allow that even stage one is a state of hypnotism, a state where you are physically relaxed and mentally quiet. Certainly it is true that this is a stage everybody can reach.

However, not everybody can be hypnotized if you set your standards higher, say to the susceptibility to posthypnotic suggestion or higher still to partial anesthesia. The degree to which a person can be hypnotized depends not only on himself but on the operator. Ninety-five percent of the subjects of a fully skilled operator can be brought to the posthypnotic suggestion stage, eighty percent to the anesthesia stage, and perhaps forty to sixty percent all the way.

Sometimes a person's susceptibility to suggestion is limited via hypnotism, but quite open through other means. Recently, the case of June Clark, a seventeen-year-old Miami High School sophomore who was racked with compulsive sneezes every four minutes of every waking hour, received nationwide publicity. The mysterious malady baffled neurologists, allergists, nose and throat specialists, internists, and psychiatrists.

Finally hypnotism was used. Despite her being a relatively good subject and reaching an adequate depth of hypnosis, suggestions to stop sneezing failed to work. What did work after nearly six months that brought head and chest pains, nausea, fatigue, and muscle spasms was the administering of electric shocks. Electrodes were attached to June's forearms and a microphone was hung around her neck. When she sneezed, a voice key triggered a mild electric shock through her arms. In four hours the sneezing had stopped.

The same motivating subconscious that was reached in hypnosis and failed to respond to the spoken word, reacted immediately to the reward and punishment technique. June's sneezes had been rewarding. They made her the center of attention and brought her sympathy from people all over the world. The shocks changed this reward to punishment. At the end of the first hour her sneezing rate was down from 44 to 20 per hour. Then it dropped to 6, 1, and finally none. Where tranquilizers, antihistamines, and other medication—including hypnosis—had failed, the simple principle of spanking a child when bad and rewarding her with candy when good had succeeded.

Everybody is open to suggestion to a degree. Hitler built his Germany on this premise. Political campaigns are won or lost on how well they harness the power of suggestion. Advertising, from giant billboards to the living room television screen, represents billions of dollars invested in the power of suggestion.

You can evaluate your own suggestibility by the standard pendulum test. Attach a button to the end of a nine-inch length of string. Sit at a table and place your right elbow on it with the end of the string in your hand. Let the pendulum hang free with the button just clearing the tabletop. Sit very quietly and relaxed. Now visualize the pendulum swinging slowly back and forth. Use your mind's eye to will it to move. You are now giving yourself a suggestion. If you are highly susceptible, the suggestion will work on the first try. The pendulum will start to move just as you visualize it moving, and without any conscious effort to move it with your hand.

Another test for suggestibility can be taken in a standing position, with your back to a wall, about two inches from it. Stare slightly upward at the ceiling, then close your eyes and imagine that the wall has developed a magnetic force that gets stronger and stronger. As you count to ten, the pull gets stronger on your back until you can no longer resist it. You are likely to touch the wall before you reach the count of ten.

Or try the shopping bag test. It goes like this: Sit in a straight-back chair with your arms held horizontally in front of you. Close your eyes and visualize somebody placing the handle of a full shopping bag over your left wrist. Wait for about one minute as you "feel" the heavy load tire your arm and "see" it begin to lower. Then open your eyes. Your autosuggestion has probably placed a good few inches between your two arms.

Who Can Be a Hypnotist

The percentage of persons who can hypnotize themselves is just as high—nine out of ten—as those who can be hypnotized by others, for you will perceive as your understanding grows that all hypnotism is self-hypnotism. However, all self-hypnotists are not necessarily capable of hypnotizing others.

Sigmund Freud recognized the therapeutic value of hypnotism, but because he was not adept at hypnotizing many of his patients to a sufficient depth to uncover the traumatic memories he sought, he usually sidestepped hypnosis in favor of an analytic approach.

Even if Freud had mastered the science of hypnotism, he would still have had much to learn about the art of hypnotism. His technique of managing the state of hypnosis was characterized by authoritatively removing symptoms with the subjects in a state of somnambulism. Undoubtedly other strategic means were available on the spot depending on the subject's reaction. Had he devoted to hypnotism the briliance he applied to the other psychological sciences, work in this field would surely have been measurably advanced.

It was Freud who once said that hypnosis gives the hypnotist authority never possessed by priest or miracle man. Certainly, the ability to hypnotize carries with it a serious responsibility. The hypnotist can make pronounced changes in the mental and physical status of the individual. It is this power that keeps many people fearful of hypnosis despite their increased interest in it. Many are the stories of sexual domination and of master-slave relationships, of the ability to control a subject for evil purposes. Most of these tales are fantasy or highly exaggerated, but they nevertheless point up the fact that misuse of hypnotic power is possible.

The primary prerequisite of a hypnotist is, therefore, a sense of responsibility. He should realize the critical nature of hypnosis and appreciate the effects that every spoken word can have on the health and well-being of the subject. His professional attitude should extend beyond the medical disciplines to encompass psychological and social ethics. He must protect the welfare and respect the integrity of his subject.

Anybody can be a hypnotist. He does not have to have piercing eyes or a commanding voice. The attributes of knowledge and skill far exceed any such physical factors. Even the mildest Mr. Milquetoast can induce hypnosis in the roughest and toughest character through proper management of induction techniques. Women can be hypnotists as readily as men, young adults as readily as older persons.

A "Hypnotist Wanted" ad might well read: "Person wanted who can help another person to fix his attention on an object such as a watch, metronome, whirling disc, or spot on the wall and tell him in a soothing and lulling voice that his eyes are getting heavy and his entire body is becoming deeply relaxed."

On the other hand a "Clinical Hypnologist Wanted" ad would seek: A man trained in induction, suggestion, and termination procedures who devotes full time to the practice of hypnotherapy and whose knowledge of basic psychology permits him to develop the necessary rapport with his subject to motivate acceptance of beliefs.

Lest we forget, the original hypnotist—the snake—is still around. Music hypnotizes; so do lights flashing by a driver on a highway at night; so does the sound of any person speaking. Anything, as well as anyone, that can divert the attention and hold it in uncritical captivity hypnotizes.

At a New York City clinic for would-be nonsmokers, participants were shown a movie of an operation for lung cancer. It was in full color and showed every surgical and anatomical detail. It struck home—home being the subconscious. Viewers' stomachs were turned against to-bacco and their mental computers were reprogrammed. A live hypnologist could have done no better.

How Behavior Is Affected in the Hypnotized State

"Mr. Jones, after you open your eyes you will raise your hand to your head."

The hypnologist has just given a suggestion to test a subject placed in a light state of hypnosis. When the state has been terminated, he will watch carefully to see if the suggestion is carried out. Mr. Jones is out of it now. He is discussing the session. "I remember the suggestion you gave me," he says; "do you mind if I ignore it?" "Not at all," says the hypnologist. He rose to get his appointment book, keeping an eye on Mr. Jones in the wall mirror. Mr. Jones gave his hair two quick brushes with his hand.

The previous client had raised his watch to eye level

to see the time and deftly touched his forehead with his little finger. Another client scratched behind his ear. In one way or another even the simplest of suggestions in the lightest of trances must be discharged. They apparently plague the unconscious until they are dissipated by compliance. Resolve be damned, you cannot be happy or comfortable until you touch your head!

This is the mildest of phenomena producible in the hypnotic state—so mild it can be produced in many people without hypnosis. A ten-year-old boy asks what suggestion is. He is told that he will touch the roof of the car they are driving in before they reach home. "It doesn't work," he says as they approach the house, "I didn't touch the roof. But I'm going to touch it now just to finish this." The suggestion did "work," but because it was carried in the conscious mind, it was successfully resisted consciously for a while. But then the psychologists' law of inverse effect took over. The harder you try, the greater the chance that you will fail. Ask anybody who tries to resist the gustatory suggestions of sweet, and fattening, food or any other temptations.

By contrast, a suggestion planted through hypnotism in the subconscious usually bypasses conscious critical analysis. It automatically takes place despite logical evaluation. "Promptly at 11 A.M. you will take off your left shoe. You will not remember that I have told you to do so." The session is over. The hypnologist remarks that it is 11 A.M. Like an automaton the subject unties and removes his left shoe. "Why did you take off your shoe?" "I don't know, I just felt like it."

Obeying a posthypnotic suggestion is a compulsion. A hypnologist must keep careful inventory of all suggestions given to his subject and make certain that their influence is thoroughly counteracted before the subject leaves. Take for instance the suggestion given to the subject to induce hypnosis. "You are very relaxed. With every breath you take you get more and more deeply relaxed." There will be one extremely drowsy subject that day, unless the termination of hypnosis includes the suggestion, "When I clap my hands you will feel wide awake, energetic, and alert."

The mind's obedience to suggestion is the key to all that follows in the state of hypnosis. We saw how the mild suggestion of "Touch your head" cannot be denied.

Next, the "Take off your shoe" type of suggestion is automatically followed. Let us open the suggestion box and see just how far the mind will go in carrying them out.

Will the mind accept the suggestion that it will go into a deeper stage of hypnosis next time? Yes. Faster? Yes. Will the mind accept the suggestion to become less depressed and more optimistic? Will it reform kleptomania? Transform a sexual deviate? Yes, yes, yes.

Will the mind hallucinate various environmental conditions? Yes, the person will actually live whatever conditions are called for in the suggestion.

Can the mind control bodily functions on suggestions? Yes, many, even those seemingly unrelated to mental control, such as the heartbeat, bleeding, etc.

Just how far will the mind go? Let us see.

3

Doorway to Hidden Recesses of the Mind

You are sitting in a hypnologist's office. He is at his desk. You are in a chair at the far corner. You are both waiting for a patient to arrive. You do not know this man, but he has agreed to permit an observer to sit in on his first full hypnotism session. And you are the lucky one.

He is due any minute now. It is not his first visit. In fact, it is his third. He was in for the first time a little over a week ago. He is a salesman, age forty-two. He discussed his problem with the hypnologist—he has high blood pressure, is nervous, jumpy, quick-tempered. It was costing him his friends, his sleep, and his health. Yes, he was willing to follow the hypnologist's instructions and to cooperate in every way possible. Yes, he understood hypnotism, but, no, he never was hypnotized. Yes, he would be willing to return in a few days for initial tests.

The second visit was scheduled for that same week. The hypnologist explained how he was going to test to determine how good a subject the man was, and to identify the procedures to which he responded best. He led the subject through a number of exercises involving arm lifting, eye closing, and finger moving. Then there was a brief hypnosis session to confirm the results and to give the man a preview of what was coming.

The bell rings. He's here. The hypnologist introduces you and then the two are seated and you are forgotten.

A Hypnotism Session Begins

Hypnologist: Before we begin, do you have any further questions?

Mr. X.:   Well, yes. You know, after I left I started to think about the last session. Frankly, I don't think I was hypnotized. What makes you think I was?

Hypnologist: While I was testing you for the best method of induction, I noticed that you responded better to one than another. Remember, after you had relaxed, I suggested that your index finger would rise? There was then an involuntary twitch of the finger which I pointed out to you.

Mr. X.:   Yes, I remember but—

Hypnologist: Also, remember I asked you to hold your arms level and then suggested that your left arm felt light and your right arm felt heavy? What happened?

Mr. X.:   I guess one went up slightly and the other down slightly.

Hypnologist: That's right. The suggestion caused a deviation of about eight to ten inches in the arms. Well, this was the beginning of hypnosis. Had I continued instead of terminating the session, a state of hypnosis could have ensued. So today we will pick up where we left off. Are you ready?

Mr. X.:   Ready.

Hypnologist: All right, sit comfortably and place your hands on your thighs. Move around until you are sure you are in a really comfortable position. That's fine. Now look down at your left hand. Breathe a little more deeply than you would normally, as if

you were pretending that you were asleep.
Deep, regular breaths. Good. Relax as
much as you can. Let every muscle become
limp. Keep your eyes on your left hand.
Relax your feet, your legs, your whole
body. Allow your shoulders to become
limp. Relax even the small muscles of your
face. Let your jaw drop slightly, relax your
mouth, your cheeks.

Don't reply, but I would like to point out
to you some sensations that you are probably feeling in your left hand, but which
you may not be aware of. As you look
at it, it appears still. It is. It is quite
warm, and appears to be very light, listless.
Although it is still, you know there is
movement. Blood is circulating through its
veins and there are tiny nerve movements.
Soon you will see one of your fingers
make an ever so slight movement. It might
be your thumb, your little finger, your
index finger. There, you see. Your index
finger just moved.

Now your eyes might be heavy and you
may feel somewhat drowsy, but don't close
them. At least not just yet. Concentrate
on your finger movement. Soon you will
see something else happen. You will see
that your fingers will tend to spread apart.
Keep your eyes on them. And keep getting
more and more relaxed. Now you are beginning to go into a very relaxed stage of
hypnosis. You find that your left hand is
lighter, very much lighter. But your right
hand is heavier and will continue to get
heavier still.

I want you now to pay attention to your
breathing. As you inhale deeply, note the
upward movement of your chest and
shoulders. With every breath you will find
a lightness in your left arm. As you
breathe in, your chest lifts, your shoulders
lift, your arm lightens. Your hand is getting very light. See, it is hardly touching

your lap now. It is actually lifting up. Soon it will be moving still higher toward your face. You know that the closer it comes to your face the more deeply you will be in a state of hypnosis. You may close your eyes now. But keep visualizing your hand lifting toward your face.

(Mr. X. closes his eyes.)

You are now much more relaxed, more attentive to my voice. You listen to everything I say. Your hand is almost touching your face. You are approaching a wonderfully deep, relaxed state of hypnosis. Now your hand is touching your face. You are in a deep state of hypnosis. You may choose to keep your hand there, or you may return it gently to your lap.

(Mr. X. keeps his hand touching his face. It is what the hypnologist expected. Most patients do.)

Health Dealing Suggestions Are Launched

About twenty minutes have already transpired. It has been a boring, repetitive process. As an observer you yourself have had to strive to keep from getting too relaxed. But you note that the hypnologist seems satisfied with the way things are going. The induction phase is over and the therapy is about to begin. But first he will make a final test to make sure.

Hypnologist: You are now in a very profound state of relaxation and hypnosis. You will be amazed to know the state of depth. Notice that you have not made a single movement. You have not swallowed. You have not repositioned yourself. Notice how limp and heavy your body feels. It is a tremendous effort for you to move, speak, or do anything at all. Your right arm is so heavy, you can no longer lift it as you can in a normal waking state. See for yourself. Try to lift your right arm.

(Mr. X. is a husky, six-foot-two-inch specimen. Yet he struggles helplessly to move his right arm. He fails so completely that even the muscles barely budge. His failure is proof of the hypnologist's success. Now the posthypnotic suggestions.)

Hypnologist: Good. Now relax completely. Realize that although I have helped you to reach this stage, it is you who have been able to do it, and you can do it again. Whenever you wish to relax in the future, you will be able to sit back in your comfortable chair, place your hands on your legs, breathe deeply, and with each breath your hand will begin to lift toward your face. You will be able to repeat this exercise whenever you feel it necessary, whenever tension or nervous excitement needs to be quieted. The only change will be that when you have finished, you will be able to terminate the state by simply lowering your hand to your lap.

(This is the crux of the whole session. Everything that has gone before has prepared the way for this suggestion to be planted deep within the subconscious. Later, it will serve Mr. X. well when tension threatens. In effect, this posthypnotic suggestion will lower his tension level. He will be able to accept exciting or irritating situations without boiling over.)

Hypnologist: Now, when I count five you will awake. You will feel completely refreshed. You will feel wonderfully relaxed. One, two, three, four . . . at the next count you will be wide awake, refreshed, relaxed. Five— wake up now!

(Mr. X. lowers his hand. His eyes remain closed for a moment, then he opens them.)

Hypnologist: How do you feel?
    Mr. X.:   Fine.
Hypnologist: I noticed you kept your eyes closed for a moment. Why?

Mr. X.:   I enjoyed it so, I hated to end it. (He
             stretches.) Five minutes isn't enough.
Hypnologist: But thirty-five minutes is.
Mr. X.:   It was that long? It certainly didn't seem
             so.

The Suggestion Does Its Work

Before Mr. X. leaves, he is reminded to practice this relaxation for a few minutes each day. He will pick a comfortable chair in a quiet room and go through the same
procedures which, incidentally, he remembers quite
clearly.

He proved to be a good subject. His motivation was
strong. He practiced. He kept his future appointments
at which similar sessions were held. The sessions went
faster, as did his practice sessions. It took seconds to reach
a deep state of relaxed hypnosis. As he put it: "I sat
down, got comfortable, and my arm swept up to my face."

After five sessions over a period of three weeks, Mr.
X. reported to his physician that he was sleeping better
and that he was more understanding and less irritable.
Even his friends had commented on the change. He
seemed easier to get along with, was more placid, tolerant, amenable, and considerate. The report from his
physician seemed a foregone conclusion: blood pressure
was down fifteen points.

The reader is warned once again that the procedure
which proved successful in this case can be harmful in
others. It should not be attempted by anyone or on anyone. It represents an induction method chosen because it
was effective and safe for this particular subject when
used together with an observed and managed hypnosis
session.

As mentioned before, the key to any hypnosis session
is the posthypnotic suggestion given. In the case of Mr.
X. the suggestion was aimed at lowering his blood pressure. Note, however, that the suggestion was not directed
at the blood pressure, but at the attitudes that were causing the high pressure. This same principle can be used
successfully to combat all so-called psychosomatic illnesses
—physical disorders that stem from emotional and personality factors.

It can be used successfully to rid a person of unwanted

habits, to remove mental blocks that prevent normal behavior, and to add motivation to insure a desired behavior.

In all of these cases, suggestions are more effective when they seek to change the causative emotions rather than the unwanted physical symptom or the unwanted behavior pattern. As we will see later, though, if these emotions are unknown, the direct frontal attack should not be ignored.

But let us get back to Mr. X. and pinpoint some of the significant aspects of the session which contributed to its success. First of all, Mr. X. was convinced hypnosis could help him. He was anxious to be hypnotized, but he was not sure he could be.

If he had any fears or misconceptions about what to expect while in hypnosis, his desire to improve his health and well-being was certainly more important to him. Preliminary discussions dissipated some of these fears and built up a friendship and trust with the hypnologist. This is essential in almost any relationship—not only between patient and physician, psychologist, or psychiatrist, but also between student and teacher or client and lawyer.

In hypnosis this rapport is especially important in that lack of it can stand in the way of successful induction. Mr. X. felt close enough to the hypnologist to confide his suspicion that he was never really hypnotized the first time. Had he kept this to himself, it would have seriously interfered with the success of this session. Instead of concentrating his attention on his left hand, he would be dividing his attention between his left hand and the fact that the whole session was a failure to begin with.

How a Trance State Begins

Full attention to his hand caused Mr. X. to undergo a progressive restriction of consciousness. He became less and less concerned with anything else. His body was comfortable and was not clamoring for attention. There were no sounds, smells, or sights that were competing for attention. Even the hypnologist's voice was repetitive and monotonous enough so as not to intrude on this "no consciousness." If not misdirected, the conscious mind would later intercept suggestions and decide whether or not to accept them or reject them. It would turn out to be no more than a conversation with a friend in which a "Why don't you take my advice and . . ." situation would exist. Such situations happened daily in Mr. X.'s life and had no effect. No, the critical mind is the culprit and must be misdirected if therapy is to succeed.

There are other ways of attracting the conscious mind to fix its attention and thus to restrict itself. One of the most common is the use of an object such as a coin or key which is held ten to twelve inches from the eyes. At this distance the eyes must converge to focus properly on the object so that distraction from peripheral vision is limited. Some hypnologists use a card with a black spot on it. There are many devices on the market that purport to be "hypnosis machines." But whether they are of the twirling disc or metronome variety, or whether they are shiny objects that reflect light in different ways, they do little more than afford a convenient focusing point for the conscious mind.

Another method of capturing the conscious mind so that a hypnotic trance can take over is through the so-called hypnotic eye. This probably goes back to the method used by our first hypnotist, the snake. The hypnologist stares into the subject's eyes without blinking. This takes practice. It works apparently for the same reason that a fascinating object works. It is used more commonly by the stage hypnotist who requires the stern, authoritarian control.

There are other techniques and they will be described with the above in more detail when the science of hypnotism is discussed in Chapter 11. Suffice it to say now that, once captured and detoured, the conscious mind is no longer in the main stream of consciousness. The mainstream is, instead, the subconscious.

The World of the Subconscious

Just what is exposed when the conscious mind is diverted? The answer to this can only be confused by all of the neurological and physiological language invented to define areas and functions of the brain. Sticking to unscientific terms enables visual pictures to be used in describing the subconscious world.

Animals have often been described as having a fully developed subconscious but an underdeveloped conscious. Dogs and infant humans often react similarly. The infant world and the subconscious world are also closely allied.

A mother is feeding her infant. The infant does not cooperate. The mother dangles a toy in one hand. The infant's attention turns to the toy. As soon as he is sufficiently engrossed in it, the mother shoves another spoonful of applesauce into his mouth. Or the spoon becomes a "choo choo train" and his mouth a tunnel. While this fantasy occupies the conscious, value judgments on the feeding process are suspended by the child and down goes another spoonful.

Insight into the change that takes place when the conscious mind is misdirected can be gained through a simple observation about pain. Perhaps you have already noticed that when you are suffering from a severe headache, or other pain, you cannot think about something else and experience the pain at the same time. If the telephone rings, the pain is cut off from your consciousness as the conversation occupies it. The instant you end the conversation the pain is there, just as if it had been there without interruption the entire time. The same is true of pleasure, worry, and other emotions and sensations.

If you try to observe this as a self-conscious exercise, it will not prove out. For then you are directing your conscious attention to the pain or pleasure rather than misdirecting it. It is only through recall moments later that this truism can be experienced.

We cannot consciously experience the world of the subconscious. By definition, consciousness is what we do perceive mentally, and subconscious is mental activity outside of our perception. The world of the subconscious, like the unseen portion of an iceberg, is many times as vast as the conscious mind we experience.

Within its deep recesses are the storehouse of memories, the conditioned reflexes we have acquired through experiences, and the physical skills. Stored, too, is the race intelligence acquired through millennia of evolution—knowledge about survival and perpetuation of the race which is often referred to as instinct. Allied to this is the physiological intelligence that operates bodily functions automatically—involuntary muscles, glands, lungs, heart, and other vital organs.

The subconscious world within us is not divided into separate departments with impregnable, soundproof walls between them. Ours would be a different life if such were the case. Instead, the area of the subconscious which runs the body is in continuous communication with the area of the subconscious which stores memories and experiences. It has to be.

"Run for your life!" This conscious alarm touches off a series of instantaneous activities in the subconscious. All of the circumstances surrounding the approach of the danger are recorded so that any future combination of all or part of these will send warnings up to alert the conscious mind. Simultaneously, a number of bodily functions will take place. These include the cessation of the secretion of gastric juices, closing of the pylorus (exit from the stomach), and the pouring of emergency rations of energy-producing glucose into the blood.

In prehistoric days all of these bodily reactions to fear contributed to a successful flight to safety. Today, despite the relative obsolescence of physical flight, the subconscious still orders the body to react the same way to fear. As a result, even fear of job loss, fear of competition, and other "civilized" fears bring on physical changes within us. Since there is often no physical flight to utilize the products of these changes, they remain to produce symptoms of malfunction, which we call psychosomatic illness. Different emotions—anxiety, guilt, tension—produce different illnesses.

Thus, a child who is given a clock as a special toy, and then is left alone for a long time, experiences acute insecurity and later connects it with the clock. He can go into tantrums at the sight of a clock after that. Years later, as an adult, he may wonder why a look at the clock gives him a "butterfly" stomach.

The world of the subconscious is a world of infinite memory. It is a world of infinite associations. It is a world of unlimited learning. But it is also a world of no reason, no intelligence, no judgment.

Forty Trillion Circuits

The subconscious is a giant computer, estimated to have forty trillion circuits. It is programmed by our conscious mind, by all experiences awake and asleep, and by the great inherited race memory of past subconscious storage.

It does your bidding whether it makes sense or not. You can learn dates incorrectly and you will subsequently remember them just as incorrectly as you learned them. You can acquire somebody else's golf stance and never play the game to your own fullest potential.

With his conscious mind sidetracked by concentration on his left hand, Mr. X. could have been told there was a vicious dog about to attack him. He would then cringe with terror and prepare to defend himself.

He could be told that there was a raging blizzard with near zero temperatures. You would see him slap his arms to keep warm and wipe the imaginary snow from his eyes.

He could be told that he was on a stage at Radio City Music Hall without his clothes on and you would see him take immediate steps to modesty.

He could be told that he is three years old and must recite a poem. "Mary had a little lamb" would come forth in his own bygone baby talk.

These reactions are so novel, so magical, so striking that they are used as entertainment. These are the kinds of suggestions often fed into the giant computers of subjects who make themselves available to stage hypnotists.

Psychiatrists and the rest of the medical world have far more valuable use to make of this doorway to the subconscious than entertainment. Since the subject reacts to every suggestion with implicit fidelity as if it were true, they use this "as if" principle to re-create conditions that may uncover events of psychological significance. A psychiatrist can ask for the description of a past event now causing psychotic symptoms. A physician can reassure that health anxieties are unwarranted and they will subside. A clinical hypnologist can suggest that fattening foods no longer taste appetizing and they will become abhorrent.

Suggestions survive the hypnosis period and are acted upon weeks or months later. Mr. X. remembered the suggestions given him, but had they been combined with the suggestion that he would not remember them, he would still engage in the relaxation exercises but he might not know the reason why!

Memory That Knows No Bounds

The race memory department of the subconscious is credited with the phenomenon where a previous life is apparently recalled. An example of this took place before one hundred people at a demonstration in November 1965, when American Broadcasting Company news commentator Pat Michaels hypnotized a perfect stranger at a San Diego gathering. The subject was a young navy wife, aged twenty-two, who was then regressed and began to talk of her life as a fourteen-year-old during the eighteenth century when she lived in a French province. She knew no French, yet told the story in perfect French, speaking fluently and without a trace of accent!

There have been many recorded case histories of apparent memory of a previous life. The author has had a similar experience with a young teacher who was having trouble with her ability to concentrate. Because there was apparently some traumatic experience in her past that was acting as a block, she was regressed to a younger and younger age. At six years, she spoke like a child, at three, like a baby.

Suddenly she began to talk in a strange Old English manner. Asked where she was she said she was in England. When was this? In the middle of the eighteenth century. This is an unnerving experience even for a veteran hypnologist. Steps were taken to terminate the session as promptly as possible. Then, with her permission, a psychologist and a historian were asked to attend the next session.

Once again regression led to an account of an eighteenth-century life. Both professional witnesses took notes energetically. In addition, the session was taped. She told how she was an orphaned waif, adopted by a peasant family and raised as a scullery maid in a country mansion. It was a sordid life, but details were supplied in abundance that afforded material which the historian could research. A cult to which she belonged turned out to be a small one, but one that was recorded in some old source book. She told of crossing the river Avon by foot, now impossible. Research disclosed, however, that it was possible at that point in that year. And so it went for a number of intriguing sessions, explainable only by some long since forgotten exposure to such information by a teacher, by incredibly ingenious play-acting, by reincarnation, or by that race memory held in trust by the magnificent subconscious. Further details of this fascinating case are provided in Chapter 10.

Physical Changes That Are Possible

The famous magician Harry Houdini is said to have been a master at self-hypnosis and many of his apparently superhuman feats were said to have been accomplished while he was in that state. Certainly this must have been the case when, after being handcuffed and submerged through a hole cut in the Hudson River ice, he found himself yards downstream before he could free himself and swim back upstream to the opening in the ice. Expert swimmers testified that even under favorable conditions such an upstream swim would be almost impossible.

Human beings are capable of performance beyond the understanding of the conscious mind. When that self-limiting consciousness is sidetracked momentarily—as in a life-and-death emergency—herculean acts have been accomplished without thought or hesitation. If there were either thought or hesitation, there probably would be no act, for critical, conscious judgment then injects its "logical" limits.

Baseball teams have improved their performances. Bowlers have upped their scores. Athletes in all realms of sports have found a greater physical performance possible through posthypnotic suggestion. In Johannesburg, South Africa, a group of thirty-two golfers under the direction of Dr. Brian Norgarb participated in an experiment to improve their putting through hypnosis. Many had positive results. One member lowered his putting average on the 9-hole course from 23 to 17.

Posthypnotic suggestions that enhance the physical are more effective when they are aimed at removing the inhibiting conscious attitudes instead of at direct physical change. If Mr. X. was given the direct suggestion that his blood pressure would drop, there is little likelihood that it would. It is possible that it would drop, especially if a deep enough state of hypnosis were attained, but then the nervous tension that was causing it would still remain and would have the last word.

The hypnotic state is no magic wand which permits the coming true of such suggestions as "I will be rich" or "I will always be healthy" or "I will dominate women." Mr. X. could improve his financial position through hypnosis by eliminating the self-doubt and uncertainty that might be interfering with his financial judgment. He could improve his health, not by direct order to the part of the anatomy affected, but by positive suggestion to transform negative, health-wrecking attitudes and emotions. He could build up his attraction to women by suggestions to build up self-confidence through emphasis on his strong personality traits.

There are many dramatic physical changes that are effected through suggestion, but these are accomplished more often than not via the memory portion of the subconscious where phobias and conflicts spawn an encyclopedia of medical ills. A woman wished to have an annoying nervous tic removed from her shoulder. It caused continuous jerking of the neck and shoulder and was proving to be socially embarrassing. Because she had this twitch for many years and because she was not prepared to remain for a number of sessions, it appeared necessary to attack the physical symptom directly. However, the clinical hypnologist recognized that in taking such a course, the cause is being permitted to remain and that the symptom is quite likely to return or to manifest itself in some other way that might be even more undesirable.

With this in mind, hypnosis was induced and the suggestion given that the tic would not disappear, but that it would move from the shoulder to the elbow. The trance was ended to check the conscious effect. There was no change, but the tic had been transferred. The subject was put back into the trance state, and the tic was now moved to the wrist, then to the little finger. Here it was allowed to remain, until some day further therapy could be used to locate the cause and root it out altogether.

The Physical Miracle

There is little risk in having a patient visualize warts dropping off, or other minor improvements in health taking place without psychotherapy as part of the hypnotherapy. But there would be a major risk in the case of a major condition.

Take the case of an eighteen-year-old girl who was declared to have eighty percent nerve deafness by her otologist. She had had perfect hearing up until she was thirteen. If you were the hypnologist, what method would you pursue once this subject was in a trance? Would you suggest "You can hear?" You would be in for a surprise, for no sooner was this young lady placed in a trance through the use of a loudspeaker and a microphone placed near her hearing aids, than the equipment was no longer needed. She could hear while in the state of hypnosis.

What is the next step? Tell her she can hear? This might cause a severe conflict with dangerous psychological effects. The author took a more conservative task. He regressed her to the age at which she became deaf.

Hypnologist:	You are at your thirteenth birthday party. You are happy. You can hear. Do you remember?
Girl:	Yes, I can hear. There are eight girls over to my house. We are playing records.
Hypnologist:	What is the next thing that you can remember?
Girl:	My father is in the hospital.
Hypnologist:	Does this have anything to do with your loss of hearing?
Girl:	Yes, I hear the phone ring. It is the doctor calling to report my father's condition. I am afraid to hear.
Hypnologist:	What happened next?
Girl:	My father died.
Hypnologist:	Now return to the present time. You are here in my office. All of this happened a long time ago. Is there any reason now why you do not want to hear?
Girl:	I don't know.
Hypnologist:	If I told you that you could hear if you wanted to, would you want to?
Girl:	Maybe.
Hypnologist:	Well, suppose you try it out. When I wake you up you will continue to hear just as well as you hear me now. Then in twenty-four hours—tomorrow at this same time, noon—you can make up your mind whether you want to continue to hear permanently. Is that agreeable?
Girl:	Yes.
Hypnologist:	All right, now when I count to five you

will wake up hearing perfectly and feeling
fine. One, two, three, four, five!

The girl's hearing was perfect. She seemed pleasantly
surprised. Her mother was overjoyed. An appointment was
made for the following day. It was noon of that next day,
when they were crossing the street to keep the appointment when, according to the mother, the girl stopped in
the middle of the street, turned to her mother and ex-
claimed, "Mother, I want to continue to hear!"

It is apparent now that a "you will hear" suggestion
could have had far different results. Even the method used
could have been improper if the father was still on the
critical list in the hospital. As you will see in the chapters
ahead, physical "miracles" can and do occur. But it is less
often through an authoritarian control than it is through
a benign, understanding permissiveness.

Thus is it essential that the clinical hypnologist have an
awareness of human problems and anxieties. He must be
sensitive to reactions, emotions, and attitudes. His sensitivity and awareness can lead to a reprogramming of the
magnificent subconscious, to a smooth dissipation of the
causes of antisocial, even murderous, behavior. He holds
the key to health, wealth, and happiness. Now let us examine how he uses it.

4

Hypnotism in Surgery, Obstetrics, and Dentistry

One of the first medical uses for hypnotism was in surgery. At the time that hypnotism was struggling to throw off the stigma of charlatanism, anesthesia had not yet been discovered. Liquor was the only painkiller known to medical science in the mid-1800s. Needless to say, persons facing operations were terrified. Many died of shock and pain. Others screamed and struggled, making the task of the surgeon extremely difficult. The possibility of the painless surgery offered by hypnotism was enough to make doctors and patients alike reach out for it despite its tarnished image. The statistics of four fatalities out of ten during surgery had a way of opening the mind to experimentation.

A physician by the name of Parker is said to have performed two hundred painless operations at Exeter, England. At the same time Esdaile in India reported to the Medical Board seventy-five operations performed successfully and painlessly through hypnotism. His work was investigated by a committee appointed by the Deputy Gov-

ernor of Bengal. The report was entirely favorable. Esdaile
soon raised his total to three hundred major surgical operations and thousands of minor operations.

By 1891 the British Medical Association admitted in a
published report that hypnotism was frequently effective
in relieving pain and alleviating functional ailments. Today, of course, that group has expanded its endorsements
of hypnosis, as have other medical associations, to include
approval of its use in the treatment of psychoneuroses, as
anesthesia for relief of pain in surgery and childbirth, and
other therapeutic areas.

In Parker and Esdaile's day, scholars were at work de-
ciphering Egyptian literature, thanks to the keys provided
by the discovery of the Rosetta stone, and were learning
how ancient Egyptians had used hypnosis for anesthesia
and how they kept a metaphysician standing by at all
such operations to prevent the subject's body from being
possessed or violated by a discarnate spirit.

Also, while Parker and Esdaile were performing their
painless operations, nitrous oxide was making the rounds
of tent shows as "laughing gas." Quite accidentally it was
discovered that the gas not only caused great hilarity but
it also produced a state of general anesthesia. Horace
Wells, a Hartford, Connecticut, dentist, had a colleague
extract one of his teeth using "laughing gas" as anesthesia. "Not a prick of a pin" did he feel, he reported afterward. Chemical anesthesia had arrived, and hypnotism
had lost ground. Once more it was left to struggle against
the quicksands of obscurity.

Great advances have been made in anesthesia, and great
advances have been made in hypnotism. Today hypnotism
is finding wider medical use in surgery than ever before.
There are three major areas where it is in popular usage:
in alleviating pre-operative tension, as a substitute for
chemical anesthesias, and in ameliorating post-operative
conditions.

Pre-operative tension is recognized as a dangerous block
to successful surgery. Fear of the knife, fear of never
awakening from the anesthesia, fear of feeling pain com-
prise the terror that plagues the person facing an operation. Medical records are replete with case histories where
this terror has sown the seeds of its own substantiation.
Fear breeds tension; tension, incapacity and malfunction.

A person can die of fright even though the operation is a success.

Many people do not respond to the tranquilizers used by physicians to produce a necessary pre-operative calm. Some are allergic to them. Others react in reverse and become almost violent. A surgeon phoned the author one morning. A hysterectomy patient was very upset and was not reacting to tranquilizers. The operation was crucial, but the woman was so nervous that its success was in jeopardy.

The author went to the hospital directly and found the woman in a state of terror. She was actually stiff with fear. Her eyes bulged. By first divesting himself of any connection with the operation and explaining he was there only to alleviate her acute nervousness, he was able to gain her confidence sufficiently to administer a progressive relaxation procedure, similar to that described in the previous chapter.

The patient responded well to suggestions that she would remain relaxed and would experience no discomfort. You could see her muscles let go as her mind no longer dwelled on calamity. Later, sedation was used and this time it worked, enabling the operation to proceed successfully.

Hypnotism enters the operating room too. It can either enter side by side with the anesthetist or alone as a substitute for standard anesthesias. Using them together as a team enables a surgeon to cut down considerably on the use of anesthesia, thus diminishing any unwanted physiological conditions arising from the anesthesia and lessening aftereffects from it.

Where a patient is allergic to applicable anesthesias, or where the level of physical stamina makes the use of anesthesia an added risk, hypnotic anesthesia can be used alone. A patient with low blood pressure dare not use most chemical anesthesias. High fevers also make their use dangerous. Gaseous anesthesias are *verboten* for patients with lung diseases. But all may freely use hypno-anesthesia. It can provide complete protection against pain. It can permit conscious awareness of what is transpiring, if this will benefit the control of the operation, and it can close the curtain of memory and prevent any recollection of the operation.

Hypnologist in the Role of Anesthetist

How is a patient prepared for surgery under hypnoanesthesia? It all starts many days before the operation. Remember that Mr. X. needed several sessions before a good rapport could be developed, the proper induction method selected, and a fairly deep stage of hypnosis attained. The same is true for pre-surgical preparation. In fact, even more sessions may be needed to insure the deepest stage possible.

Once a deep stage is reached, the hypnologist tests the results of anesthesia-producing suggestions. Usually using the left or right hand, he goes through a series of preambles involving warmth and heaviness. Then he describes a feeling of numbness, associating it with any numbness which the patient can recall from his own past experience. Perhaps he had had a tooth extraction where novocaine had numbed the gums. "This same numbness is enveloping your hand. It is like a glove. You can feel pressure, but no pain. If I were to prick your wrist with a needle, you might feel something like a blunt pencil eraser, but you would not feel the point of the needle. Let us demonstrate this gently."

Next, the hypnologist takes a sterile hypodermic needle and touches the skin without piercing it. The suggestion of "no pain" is repeated. Asked what he feels, the patient describes pressure, like being touched with a finger, but no sensation of a needle's point. There is no withdrawing of the hand, flinching, or other pain reflex.

With this test successfully passed, the hypnologist tests further. Gently the needle is pushed into the skin. Again, the assurances of "no pain" are given to sink into the subconscious where they automatically shut off pain signals to the area in question. A needle stuck in the other hand would prick as it always does. No numbness is produced in any other part of the body at this point, only in the hand selected.

Assured that satisfactory anesthesia has been produced in the hand, the hypnologist must then get to the problem at hand and cause the same analgesic state in the part or parts of the body to be operated upon. He has two ways of accomplishing this. He can cause the numbness in the hand to be transferred to another part of the body through suggestion. Or he can start all over and use the same tested method to create the same numbness wherever it is desired by the surgeon.

In the case where glove anesthesia is to be transferred to the breast or abdomen, for example, the patient is told to place the anesthetized hand on that area. "As you touch your breast (abdomen) the numbness you have in your hand will be transferred to that part of your body. You will have the same freedom from pain there. You may feel pressure, but no pain. At the same time, feeling will return to your hand."

Often the surgeon will take part in this session. He may use a device to measure pain level. One of these is a Feridic brush that sends out electric jolts to any area of the body it touches. In this way, the surgeon can determine that the entire area which will be affected by the operation is properly desensitized. To help toward this end, he may use a crayon to trace the pressure points that will be involved in the incision and internal cutting. Thus the patient can be instructed to transfer his hand numbness to the exact points of surgical activity as traced out on his or her skin.

Surgeon in the Role of Hypnologist

Now another job of transference can take place. The hypnologist can transfer his own success with the patient over to the surgeon. "Dr. Jones is here. He is going to squeeze your wrist. Did you feel it? Now, whenever Dr. Jones squeezes your wrist in the future, you will instantly attain this deep state of trance-like relaxation, and you will enjoy numbness in the same part of your body that you have it now."

That is all there is to it. The surgeon is now in control. The posthypnotic suggestion that a squeeze of the wrist by Dr. Jones will result in anesthesia of the breast or abdomen will last days or weeks. Should a nurse or intern inadvertently squeeze the wrist, say while taking the pulse, there will be no effect. It must be Dr. Jones.

Should a last minute change of plans require a different surgeon, the hypnologist must be called in once more to make the proper suggestion that will transfer use of the "open sesame" command to the new surgeon.

Not only is the doctor imbued with the power of anesthetizing the patient by a literal flick of the wrist, but he is also empowered with the ability to make the anesthesia last as long as he finds it necessary. The patient is given the suggestion that the numbness will persist until the suggestion is given by the doctor that the numbness will end.

He can elect to hold the numbness just a few hours after the operation is over, or he may wish to retain it for days to permit healing to occur before feeling is restored. In any case the trance state is ended, but the numbness is continued as a posthypnotic effect.

The surgeon is captain of the ship during an operation. It is essential that control be transferred by the hypnologist to him so that he can move swiftly to carry out techniques and to meet emergencies. The surgeon may prefer to have the hypnologist present during the operation as an added precaution. But it still will be the surgeon who will squeeze the wrist to commence anesthesia, who will decide whether another anesthesia should be used in conjunction with hypnosis, and who will order the patient to cooperate where such cooperation is an aid to the procedure.

When the help of a patient in hypnoanesthesia is needed, the surgeon merely gives the suggestion that the subject can open his eyes, move, talk, obey instructions. Like a magic wand, the wish comes true. The miracle of hypnosis unfolds before the surgeon's eyes as he commands "Arch your back" or "Bear down." The patient responds completely and cooperatively. A general anesthesia was never like this.

To prevent possible shock in certain cases, the surgeon or hypnologist also gives the suggestion that "You will not remember anything that has taken place during the operation." Again, the wish becomes fact.

However, it is not all necessarily smooth going for the surgeon-turned-hypnologist. Some subjects have been known to request the hypnologist at the last moment despite transferral suggestions. Many subjects are extremely open to any conversation during an operation and a careless remark can be quite damaging. A remark such as "I see trouble here" has been known to cause prolonged anxiety. A note of urgency in instructions to nurses can also be unnerving to the subject. Hypnotism is not foolproof. It must be managed with skill. And as the surgeon may find out on rare occasions, hypnotism can fail. A trance can end prematurely due to unknown or unexpected conditions. Even if the hypnologist is present, chemical anesthesia should be on standby.

Painless Post-Operative Days

After the operation is over, the surgeon may elect to retain the numbness. He may also wish to provide special help to the patient in the post-operative period. "This area will remain numb. You will be able to lie quietly in one position for many hours without feeling any discomfort. You will wake up at the count of three. You will have no feeling in the area, no desire to change your position. One, two, three."

If pain is a necessary danger signpost for the surgeon or physician, a dull pain may be permitted to gain entrance through the amazing doors of hypnosis. Thus the patient's report of a dull pain can be interpreted and acted upon accordingly by the medicos.

Patients who must be kept in traction can be made more comfortable despite the lack of movement. The surgeon can give the necessary suggestion for this either during or after the operation. He may also elect to repeat it one or more times during the period of traction. This he does by rehypnotizing the patient—a fifteen-second procedure if the wrist pressure method (or equivalent) is used. "Your foot is being elevated for traction. You will not feel the elevation. Your foot will be just as comfortable as if it were in its natural state. Regardless of its elevated position, you will be comfortable. When I count to three you will awake feeling alert, refreshed, and wonderful. One, two, three."

Some surgeons utilize hypnotic procedure in cases of minor surgery such as the stitching of minor lacerations. First a bandage is placed over the eyes. Then the suggestion is made that the patient is going into a deep state of relaxation—deeper with every breath he takes. Some ask their patients to count backward to deepen the state.

It is then stated that the first stitch is being made. However, the needle is merely placed at the edge of the wound. "There, did that hurt?" The patient of course responds negatively. After another imaginary stitch, the belief of anesthesia becomes an autosuggestion and acts exactly as if the suggestion had come from the surgeon or a hypnologist. The sewing can then proceed in earnest and the patient is not likely to suspect that a misdirection of his attention had brought on a mild hypnoanesthesia.

What Is Mind?

As we begin to understand what hypnotism can do, we are likely to miss an important building block in the whole picture—the brain itself. Painless surgery through hypnotism is in effect the human voice cutting off pain via the brain. The hypnologist speaks; the subject hears; hearing produces a thought; the thought cuts off feeling.

The thought could do other things besides cutting off feeling. It could, as an activity of the brain, affect other activities of the brain. And that means working of muscles, functioning of organs, making or breaking of habits, attitudes, and emotions. All of these are activities of the brain —the organ within the skull which has been described as "a swollen piece of wrinkled fruit" located at the top of our spinal column.

To understand the topography of the brain is an exercise in futility. Although some strides have been made recently, most ridges and valleys could be on the moon for all the good it does to locate and identify them. Man's knowledge about the brain and how it performs as the organ of thought, sensation, and movement is in its infancy.

"What is the mind? No matter. What is matter? Never mind!" The classic witticism bears out that special nature of mind which defies investigation along standard lines. As the eye cannot see itself, the mind appears not to know itself. Can we measure imagination, creativity, love, or inspiration on a potentiometer? Or the sense of good and evil?

Recently, however, new mirrors have been held up which may throw new light on those three parts of the brain known as the cerebrum, cerebellum, and medulla oblongata. Electronic computers are analyzing brain-wave data in great detail. Nucleic acids are being studied in connection with heredity and pointing to some interesting facts about memory. New mind drugs such as LSD affect the workings of the brain so drastically that new insights are revealed.

The average person who feels there is a missing link in his understanding of hypnotism feels correctly. But the link of understanding that he misses is missing also for the psychiatrists, psychologists, physicians, and hypnologists who use hypnotism.

Granted the cerebrum with its lobes and convolutions runs the body's conscious movements, its thoughts, and its memories. Granted that the cerebral cortex around it contains higher thinking facilities. Granted that the cerebellum coordinates simple movements and the medulla oblongata controls reflexes and subconscious actions. Still, how does a spoken suggestion by the hypnologist (even by the subject himself as we will learn later) turn off pain? Will the answer turn out eventually to be a number of chemical changes transferred from molecule to molecule? Or will the language of chemistry fail, and some new language have to be developed to understand such mental phenomena as the transmission and nontransmission of pain, the mobility and immobility of muscle, and the effects of anxiety, fear, insecurity, and other emotions? Until time tells, we can but use hypnotism to work its miracles and wonder why.

Hypnosis in Childbirth

One of the most intriguing and totally unexplainable phenomena connected with hypnotism is time distortion. It was discovered quite accidentally in connection with time regression, where the subject is asked to recall events that happened many years before. It was found that not only could the subject "play back" these events in the minutest detail, but could also slow or speed the process.

For instance, to demonstrate time distortion, a young expectant mother was hypnotized and asked to describe a movie she had seen from beginning to end. She was asked to give a running commentary of the picture as it unfolded in her visual imagination. This she proceeded to do. At the rate the commentary was being supplied she was "seeing" the film at its normal rate of about an hour's duration.

Next, she was asked to start over and this time speed up the process so that the hour would be telescoped into eight minutes. She would refrain from an oral commentary, but she would raise her left hand when the picture began, raise the index finger whenever the male lead entered the screen, lower it when he exited, and raise her right hand when the film ended. This she was able to do right on time. In discussing the experiment afterward, she described seeing the entire film and was amazed when it was pointed out to her that just eight minutes had elapsed.

She was intrigued to learn that actors use this time distortion in hypnosis and self-hypnosis to review their roles over and over again in a fraction of the time it would normally take. Musicians learn quicker, too, by repracticing a piece ten times visually under hypnosis in the time it would take to go through it once at the piano.

The reason this young lady was in the office was to utilize hypnotism in relieving labor pains in her forthcoming confinement. She was then told how this time distortion could be used to make the painful contractions seem like only a couple of seconds, and the restful periods in between seem many times longer than they were. Once she understood the procedure she readily agreed to it, and it was a simple matter to give her the posthypnotic suggestion that each contraction would trigger a compressuring of time and each end to a contraction would extend time. Several sessions were used to reinforce these suggestions. A couple of weeks later she enjoyed a painless birth process. She reported that she was "hardly aware of the contractions" which seemed like "sudden quick pressure with palms of the hand." This time distortion in no way affected the normal birth procedure.

There are many other ways in which hypnotism is effective in obstetrics. Used as anesthesia, through methods described earlier in this chapter, it is effective in approximately fifty percent of the cases. Even in the other fifty percent it can be helpful when used with chemical anesthesias to reduce the dosage by as much as seventy-five percent. This is especially important in obstetrics where chemicals may affect the infant. Time distortion and anesthetizing by dulling the pain can be triggered by the contractions themselves, by the hypnologist, by the obstetrician, or by the mother herself through prenatal instruction in self-hypnosis.

Hypnotism can be effective in restoring wholesome attitudes toward childbirth. Many a modern mother goes "to the post" with three autosuggestive strikes against her. She hears at an early age about the pain of child-birth from her parents, uncles, and aunts. She is all the more ready to accept the gruesome details when her older sister and her friends return from the hospital with their fresh from the torture racks report.

Next, it's her turn. Fear and tension mount. Suggestion works just as faithfully to create pain as it does to erase it. Imagine her state on entering the labor room where a half dozen women are in various stages of reacting to their own negative programming. Moans, screams, cries of "Doctor!", "Nurse!" sign her own pain warrant. Hours later her story of agony is being programmed into others to perpetuate this heritage of torment.

To attack the heritage is heresy. Yet many have dared to do so—successfully. One such human patriot was Grantly Dick Read whose "natural childbirth" method enabled thousands of women to throw off the yoke of fear and return to a level of discomfort "enjoyed" by primitive women. Carry-overs of ancient pain-free birth are still observable today in jungle societies. In Argentine villages, women go down to the river, tie the umbilical cord themselves, use their big toe to help extract the after-birth, and return to the fields hours later with the infant on their back.

The Read method helps women to approach childbirth with the knowledge that it need not be feared. It re-programs the subconscious through relaxation and suggestion procedures that are closely allied with light stages of hypnotism. Women who use the method conscientiously invariably report splendid results.

Group sessions to relieve fear about labor and delivery are common in this country and abroad. In the Soviet Union, instructions of the doctor engaged in group dynamics are similar to those of a hypnologist, and women respond in a manner suggestive of hypnotic stages. Building up belief, confidence, and positive expectation are all hypnotic techniques. But who is to say where suggestion ends and education begins? The result is the same.

Advantages of Hypnosis to Mother and Child

Besides raising the threshold of pain to a level where it may not even be reached, hypnotism delivers many other advantages to the mother, the child, and the obstetrician.

Most striking is the elimination of the dangers of pain-relieving drugs and anesthesias which medical reports confirm can reduce the oxygen supply to the fetus, causing anoxemia and possible brain damage. When one hears that infants born to drug-addicted mothers are themselves born as addicts doomed to withdrawal symptoms which some do not survive, one wonders about the effects on the infant of lesser quantities of drugs taken by the mother during pregnancy and labor.

Hypnosis reduces fatigue, minimizes exhaustion, and, in fact, usually cuts down the first stage of labor several hours. It reduces shock, decreases the need for operative delivery, and increases the mother's ability to cooperate with nature. Need for suturing of the perineum due to tearing is reduced. Speedier recovery ensues.

The joys of birth are more fully experienced through hypnotism. The mother can "live" the experience, hear her baby's first cry and be able to enjoy it. One mother brought a Polaroid camera with her. She could not see over her abdomen so she took pictures by raising the camera and obtaining instantly developed pictures of her baby being born. She used the overhead reflector for some of the shots and changed her position a number of times to get different angles.

Will a woman look forward to her confinement with a feeling of apprehension? The answer bespeaks the fact. As you think so are you. A person with rose fever walks into a room where imitation roses are part of a permanent centerpiece. Immediately a spell of sneezing ensues.

Are the sneezes real? Certainly they are. They are triggered by the subconscious on receipt of the conscious message: Roses! It means nothing to the subconscious that the conscious transmitted erroneous information. Once the mistake is discovered and the message goes to the subconscious: Not really roses!—the sneezing stops.

Are the labor pains real? Certainly they are. They are triggered by the subconscious on receipt of the conscious message: Painful contractions are beginning! It means nothing to the subconscious that here too the conscious has transmitted erroneous information. Once the truth is known and the message goes to the subconscious: Pain not really necessary!—labor becomes painless.

One expectant mother was referred to the author by her psychiatrist. She was terrified. Psychotherapy had helped, but she had become desperate and could not continue it. Her family were becoming nervous wrecks. Her husband had heard the author lecture and it was at his suggestion that hypnosis would now be tried.

She seemed anxious to talk about her fears. They did not seem to be related to any other visit to a hospital; she had never even visited a friend there. She had always been in good health and had never experienced minor surgery. No, her teeth were in good condition and she could not remember any especially painful visit to a dentist. But, yes, it was the fear of pain that plagued her.

Since she had reacted poorly to the wholesome "right perspective" approach of the psychiatrist, this was avoided and instead hypnosis was now offered to her as an "out." "It might be possible that you will have no experience of birth at all. With a good state of hypnosis you can experience no pain or discomfort."

This bait was so tempting that the young lady achieved a deep somnambulistic state of hypnosis on the first try. A system of dissociation was used: "It is often difficult to remember. For instance, where were you just three years ago today? What time did you eat lunch on that day? What did you have for lunch? You cannot remember, of course. It is possible to separate yourself from today just as you are separated from three years ago today. You can instead attach yourself to a day that you especially liked. What was such a day? You enjoyed that cottage in Cape Cod. Fine. Picture it. See the flowers. You are relaxed. You have forgotten about today and the baby and you are on the porch of your Cape Cod cottage. It is quiet. You have no fears. Now you will note that you have no sensation as you press your hand on your stomach. Will you agree to try this? If you feel any discomfort as I press on your stomach raise your right hand, and I will stop. (I press. She does not raise her hand.) You see. That did not bother you, did it? Birth will feel just like this. Will you be upset?"

She shook her head, impatient at such a ridiculous idea. How could she be upset at the mere touching of her stomach? The session was terminated. She said she felt fine, much more relaxed and that a terrible weight had been removed from her shoulders. The obstetrician was taught how to trigger this same condition by pressure on her arm, arranged through posthypnotic suggestion. She had a normal birth. When it was all over, she would not believe she had had the baby. "You are lying to me!" The proof weighed nine pounds, two ounces.

The Blessings of Hypnotism in Dentistry

Imagine sitting in a dentist's chair. The dentist places his hand on your cheek. "You will feel no pain. Open, please." He prepares for drilling, drills, fills. You feel nothing. You did not have to close your mouth, or change position. No mouth props or retentive devices were used. Salivation was reduced. Even bleeding was at a minimum —all through posthypnotic suggestions given by your hypnologist a few days before.

For years afterward, visits to the dentist can be painless, from just one good hypnosis session. Extractions can be performed, painlessly. Gag reflexes can be eliminated. Even the wearing of dentures can be made more comfortable.

All of this is, of course, no less a miracle than those of hypnotism in obstetrics. But there is no doubt that the better half of this miracle is, once more, the removal of fake conditioning to which most of us are subjected in relation to the dentist, his chair, and his lancet or drill.

U.S. Army officers discovered that when a soldier faints on a hot parade ground, there is likely to be a chain reaction. If the soldier is in the rear rank where he is not seen by the others, the occurrence would be the only one. But if the event is fully witnessed, as many as one in every five can succumb.

Airline hostesses have also noticed that if a passenger succumbs to turbulence by vomiting, it is more likely to touch off several more such cases if it occurs up in front where it is easily observed by other passengers. Seasickness is similarly "contagious."

Fear and tension ride the D.D.S. and everything connected with him. This sets the stage for pain and many a scream heard in the waiting room from inside the dentist's office has occurred before anything has yet touched a tooth.

This is not to say that dentistry is not painful. It can be excruciating. But as in childbirth, much of the "pain" that is felt is a product of conditioning. Dentists themselves recognize this and that is one of the reasons that they have been quick to utilize hypnotism not only as an anesthesia for heavy work, but also as a quick way to recondition patients to relax without fear and to throw off the expectation of pain.

Dentists themselves, though, are caught in the dilemma of wanting to use hypnotism, but having neither the time nor the interest in the study of hypnology. Enter the hypnologist. Try that cue again, louder. Never mind, it will do little good. There is no hypnologist in this town.

Dental colleges are ahead of medical colleges in correcting the lack of knowledge and skill regarding hypnotism in their profession. The education dentists are receiving about hypnotism is making a great contribution toward its understanding in other areas of medical discipline. But the main problem persists. The dentist is delighted with the ease hypnology has brought to his practice, but his practice is dentistry, not hypnology. He is willing to learn induction, suggestion, and termination procedures, but he is not willing or able to cope with the many problems along the way to which a clinical hypnologist can address himself with skill and effectiveness.

The average dentist with a fundamental knowledge of hypnotism pales at some of the strange, and surely unexpected, phenomena akin to the state of hypnosis, about which we will learn further in the chapters ahead. He pales, too, at the cost in time to prepare a patient for hypnotism.

But wait, the problem is even bigger than we think. Hypnotism is not only a boon in surgery, obstetrics, and dentistry, it is also of great help with a vast number of other physical ailments. And even if all of the psychiatrists and psychologists were ready, willing, and able to pitch in to provide hypnological assistance, the call for clinical hypnologists would still be immense. The need for hypnologists continues to mount as the areas of physical and mental illness in which hypnosis has been demonstrated to be useful continue to grow.

5

Uses of Hypnotism
in Physical Health

Hypnotism is the key to the mind. The mind, more than any other element, is the key to health. The syllogistic conclusion is starkly clear. Badgered by the harrumphing of their play-it-safe colleagues, most doctors are knowingly or unknowingly turning their backs on hypnotism's promise. The losers are the patients.

Perhaps doctors cannot be blamed. They can write out a prescription for medicine in seconds and know it will be accurately filled. They can order a variety of tests from a medical laboratory in seconds and know that the tests will be given by trained personnel and reports accurately made. But hypnotism does not come in bottles, and the hypnotism laboratory is still to be born.

Meanwhile, the blessings of cure, without risk or side effects, in many otherwise difficult to cure diseases, are for the few whose physicians have acquired the skills of hypnology and have the time and willingness to use them or whose physicians have hypnologists available to them and the professional courage to use them.

Perhaps the easiest way to understand the therapeutic aspects of hypnotism is to observe its use in a number of disorders commonly known as psychosomatic. These are illnesses that are known to be a direct result of emotions. The list is growing. Nervous stomach, ulcers, and other gastrointestinal disorders were among the first to be found to be directly related to the emotions. Decades ago, using a "window" into the stomach, doctors observed the stomach turn crimson when the patient became angry or upset. Asthma and heart disease were among the next to be placed on the list of mind-related diseases.

Today the interference that the mind exerts in the normal functioning of the body is receiving wider recognition. At a recent medical convention one speaker predicted that there will come a time when almost every disease and disorder will be attributable to attitudes or emotions.

There is a widespread misunderstanding about psychosomatic illness. "It is in your mind. You are imagining it." This is the connotation to most people of the term psychosomatic. It is not exactly the way to win the sympathy of a person doubled up with stomach cramps or prostrated by a migraine headache. Their agony may be psychosomatic. In fact, it most likely is. But that in no way makes the pain any less like pain, the misery any less unbearable, or the illness any less real. Psychosomatic illness is real illness indeed. But it is being caused not by a malfunctioning organ, and not by a foreign invader. Rather, it is being caused by prolonged emotions that are disturbing the normal functioning of the glands, muscles, or vital organs.

Tension, anxiety, worry, envy, and hate are killers. Very real killers. They may take years, but they get their man— or woman. More often than not they go unrecognized as the villain. It is not logical to connect the possibility of a contract with the Big Corporation with chronic nausea and stomach cramps. How can you tell a woman with gall bladder trouble that it is due to the emotional stress she is being subjected to over that problem with her sister. If she believed you, she would probably be too wrapped up in the problem to give it up, even if it meant surgery!

Pros and Cons of Symptom
Removal Through Hypnotism

Hypnotism can be used to attack the symptom directly or to attack the emotional causes behind the symptom. Symptom removal is often labeled as dangerous on the grounds that new and perhaps more dangerous secondary symptoms may replace the original or primary symptom. This can happen occasionally, but in the author's experience it is the exception rather than the rule. After all, most medicines are prescribed to remove symptoms with hardly any thought to possible successors.

One of the advantages of hypnotism in symptom removal is that if a new symptom did arise, hypnotism could quickly reverse the process if need be and restore the original symptom.

A young man came to the author's office with an unusual physical problem. His hands dripped water. It could hardly be called perspiration because it happened in all temperatures and the water dripped at a phenomenal rate. A one-ounce whiskey glass would fill in less than an hour. He had to leave his job as an architectural draftsman and find a job as a stock clerk. He had sought psychiatric help but had become impatient with it. Medical help attacked the symptom with a medicine that was an internal dehydrator, but it did not affect his hands and only made him sick.

Conversations between the author and the psychiatrist revealed that two clues had been turned up: (1) He had been bathed by his mother until the age of thirteen or fourteen. (2) He was having difficulty in his relationships with girls. Either or both of these paths could have been pursued further through hypnoanalysis—a process of reliving certain experiences so that causative factors might be unearthed. However, it was decided instead to attack the symptom itself.

After a suitable trance state was obtained, simple suggestions were given that the hands would run less and less. Sessions were held twice a week. An immediate effect was noted. By the end of the third week the dripping had stopped. Sessions were continued for several weeks thereafter to help insure permanent removal. Did he find that the water formed anyhow and had to exit somewhere else? He did not. And even if it did, and he preferred his hands to the new egress, it would probably have been a simple matter to shift it back to the hands by similar suggestion. Note that the suggestion was not given that the symptom would cease. Small improvements were sought so that the patient's condition could be observed along the road to recovery. Even when the symptom was barely discernible the suggestion was not given to cease altogether as this could interfere with normal perspiratory functions.

Here the cause had not been removed. Yet no secondary symptom followed the primary symptom once it had been removed. Not only that, but the primary symptom remained removed even after he returned to his old job as architectural draftsman. The man lives near the author's office and through chance meetings over the past years, it has been verified that no repetition of the problem has occurred.

Symptom removal must be handled in a judicious manner just as drugs and medicines are dispensed. You would not consider attempting to remove measle rashes. You might succeed, but they are a necessary method of excretion used by the body to eliminate poisons of the disease. You would not use hypnotism to eliminate pain completely. You might succeed, but you may be eliminating a vital danger signal.

Symptom removal is safest where the cause is without a doubt attributable to emotional factors and where the initiating events are in the past. The young girl who regained her hearing after one hypnosis session, as related in a previous chapter, may not have relinquished this symptom as quickly immediately after her father's death as she did five years later. In her case the symptom was a necessary defense. To have robbed her of this defense at a time when she needed it would probably have resulted in its quick return or the creation of a new defense. As her need for this symptom was melting away, her belief in its permanence was building up. This is a common occurrence. It is the reason why temporary symptoms can become permanent conditions via autosuggestion.

The clincher in a decision to remove a symptom of psychosomatic origin is the patient's own attitude. If he is forced by family or social pressure to seek therapy, secondary symptoms are more likely to arise. On the other hand if he is actively seeking therapy of his own volition, it is more likely that he is ready to relinquish the symptom once and for all.

The Removal of Gastrointestinal Symptoms

"Don't worry." This friendly advice falls like rain on the nation's ears every day. It bears the intended inference that everything will turn out all right. Somehow the inference never comes off. The worrier finishes the thought as "Don't worry today, things will get worse tomorrow." Misuse of the imagination has a way of perpetuating itself with compound interest. Where the misuse has to do with worry and anxiety, the payoff is stomach disorder.

The mass of evidence about which kinds of emotional tensions cause which kinds of physical problems is building up. One day there will be an easy reference book that will list physical symptoms and the types of emotions from which they arise. There will be a reverse index in this book too, listing the kinds of troubles courted by specific emotions, i.e., hate, anger=heart trouble, gallstones. Such a book might not be useful for preventive therapy but it would be useful for identifying emotions causing physical symptoms so that these emotions might be changed with hypnotism.

One entry in such a book would be: Worry and tension produce gastrointestinal disorders. The human alimentary canal, starting with the mouth, and proceeding through the throat, esophagus, stomach, into the intestines, rectum, and anus, is lined with muscles. The mouth alone has ordinary striated muscles under voluntary control. The rest of this long digestive tract has two sets of smooth muscles. One set is circular, surrounding the tract; the other set runs lengthwise. Both are involuntary muscles controlled by the subconscious. Their interaction forces the "milking" action that churns and moves the food we eat along the tract until it is expelled.

Who needs a stomachache? The answer is nobody. Stomach disorders are not usually defenses thrown up by the body to protect itself. There was something the deaf girl did not want to hear. Deafness was her defense. However, those who have researched the connection between the worry and the ulcer are pretty much agreed that congested intestinal linings, strangled veins, muscular spasms, and ultimate destruction of the intestinal lining all arise from excessive acidity and other physiological imbalances, but they are pretty much in disagreement as to just how waves of guilt can cause intestinal muscle spasms, or just how anxiety affects acid flow.

Were these emotions to be exposed to the cold light of reason, they would very likely disappear. This is, perhaps, where defense may be said to be at work. The subconscious mind refuses to divulge its peeves, guilts, worries, and anxieties to its conscious counterpart. Instead, they are closely guarded in the subconscious world where they produce their effects, however unexplainable, on those involuntary muscles that are its domain—muscles that operate the glands and organs that secrete digestive juices and propel the food.

A young man who was a hairdresser, saving up for the day when he could have his own salon, became subject to recurring attacks of what his physician diagnosed as ulcers. He had to quit his job and he decided to buy his own shop so that he could earn an income working only occasionally. Of course his financial problems increased, as did his irritability, edginess, tenseness—and ulcer attacks. Medication worked to bring relief, but it did not prevent the attacks. A bland diet prescribed to prevent the attacks did so fairly well, but as soon as he felt well, he took chances with spicy and fried foods and the result was another attack.

The recurring attacks interfered with the proper supervision of his shop and as a last resort he decided to try hypnotism. Suggestions in two directions were provided. "You will be more calm and relaxed. You will not be easily excited. You will feel more confident." This suggestion was aimed at the primary cause. "You will not eat spicy or fried foods. You will find it enjoyable and satisfying to eat the foods specified by your physician." This suggestion was aimed at the secondary cause—foods that were hard to digest because the primary cause was taking its toll of the stomach lining and other tissues.

The most immediate effect of these suggestions was a change of attitude. He became more phlegmatic and reserved. He ate right without will power. His stomach attacks lessened in intensity and frequency and, after six weeks of hypnosis sessions, ceased altogether. How long did the effect of these suggestions last? Follow-up studies are a neglected part of most private health-related practices. In this case, the hairdresser's wife came to the author for weight control and supplied the finale for this case history: As late as a year and one half later, no recurrence.

This case history is typical of thousands throughout the country. In Chicago forty ulcer patients were divided into two groups of twenty. The first group was given standard medical treatment. The second received standard medical treatment augmented by hypnotism. The result showed forty percent better progress when hypnotism was used.

Usage in Orthopedics

What is the link between mind and body? How and why does a feeling of insecurity in the mind affect a muscle or blood vessel in one's body? Little is known, but studies are accelerating. At a recent seminar at Children's Hospital in San Diego, California, pediatricians learned that lack of mother love can turn an otherwise normal child into a dwarf. Dr. Henry K. Silver, professor of pediatrics at the University of Colorado School of Medicine described how his research disclosed that children's growth became stunted when deprived of parental love, and particularly motherly love.

The pediatricians were told that short stature, excessive appetite, and a delay in bone age pointed to love deprivation. The baby will grow normally for the first year, but will eat twice as much as a normal child. Then the growth rate drops. The child will continue to eat twice as much food as normal but bone calcification will take place at a slower than normal rate. A seven-year-old can be as tall as a normal two-year-old. When psychological causes of the dwarfism are removed, the children spurt upward and can catch up to others of their own age.

If you were the hypnologist, and such a case was referred to you for treatment, just what suggestions would you give to whom? Would you hypnotize the youngster and give the suggestion that "You will grow normally" or that "You are loved dearly by your parents"? Or would you feel that hypnotism would be more effective when used on the parents? Would you suggest to them that "You love your child" or make some other approach?

Obviously it is the parents that must be treated. There is

no known substitute for parental love even if it must come from foster parents. The child cannot be long convinced subconsciously of something that does not exist in its conscious world, nor can its physiological functioning be dealt with in direct confrontation with the truth. Hypnotism has its limits. Those limits coincide with those that define reason and wisdom. The child's subconscious is doing what it can to compensate for the lack of love by producing hunger symptoms and causing the child to eat twice as much as normal. It has been demonstrated that a rag doll will be used as a mother substitute by an infant ape. But as long as the human infant's real mother is present, or a suitable flesh and blood substitute, there is where therapeutic attention should be directed.

In Dr. Silver's study, mother love was lacking for a variety of reasons. There were just too many older children; or there were two girls and this was a boy, giving the mother a feeling she could not cope with this one as she did with the others. There are many, many possible reasons, but none of them are normal or valid and all of them are based on psychological factors that can be removed. Hypnotism was not mentioned as having been used in this study, but if psychological factors cannot be speedily removed by other means, hypnotism is surely a proven technique.

Suggestions might well relate to building up the instinctive love for the child and removing the self-limitations or other negative factors that interfere with that love. "You love your child. You are confident of your love and know that nothing will ever diminish that love. You are anxious to express your love to your child in every way you can."

Not only does the mind affect the body, but the mind of one person can affect another's body. But let us return to specific physical ailments in which hypnotism can be used for therapy and continue on the subject of bones in the general area known as orthopedics—the correction and prevention of deformity.

Cases have been reported where hypnosis used in connection with the amputation of limbs has provided not only pain relief but has eliminated shock and post-operative phantom limb discomfort. Broken bones have been set and hypnotism used not only as anesthesia but also to control posthypnotically the continuous position of the limb and improve comfort for the duration of a restrictive cast. Youngsters have been reported hypnotized for orthopedic surgery to reduce psychic trauma.

Many muscular-skeletal conditions, especially in the region of the back, cannot be positively identified as due to an orthopedic cause. When psychologically examined, the conditions are often attributable to emotional causes. "Oh, my aching back" and "Get off my back" are verbalizations of typical attitudes that manifest in corresponding symptoms. The weight of guilt or of inordinate responsibility can be felt in the vertebrae. Hypnotism can be used to reprogram negative guilts and restore confidence in the ability to handle responsibility. A single session can eliminate severe backache. However, if the psychological causes are continuous or increasing, the condition will usually return unless repeated sessions are used.

Wry neck, or torticollis, is another symptom that often defies physical therapy. Sometimes said to be due to anxieties too difficult to face, but more often understood to be a constant spasm of muscles in the neck, the patient's twisted neck is quickly straightened in hypnotism through suggestions directed both at the need to relax the neck muscles and the need to be insulated from the irritation or other condition causing the anxiety.

Relief of Respiratory Ailments

In the musical comedy *Guys and Dolls*, the female lead sings a plaintive song entitled "A Person Can Develop a Cold," in which she sneezingly admits that her unmarried status may be responsible for her many colds. This song brought home to millions an understanding of what psychosomatic ailments are all about.

There may be some doubt about whether natural hypnotism can help a girl catch a man, but there is no doubt that it can help her catch a cold—or not catch a cold. "Don't sit in a draft or you'll catch a cold," "Don't go barefoot or you'll catch a cold." These suggestions administered to us in our suggestive years undoubtedly programmed many a cold symptom. We have been actually hypnotized into catching a cold. This can be demonstrated on a subject by a hypnologist if there is any doubt. He can produce many other symptoms, too, as posthypnotic suggestions in a clinical experiment. Blisters can form from imaginary burns. Coughing fits can be manifested.

But the hypnologist's role in practice is the removal of such symptoms, not their creation, and for him complete, outright removal is no experiment, but daily routine.

What about the cold germs? What about catching a cold from someone else? Here, too, we have been programmed to respond with a sore throat or a running nose when contagion seemed the order of the moment. This is not to say that such a cold is unreal. It is very real. It is not to say that no cold is ever caught. Of course colds are caught. But eliminate emotional factors and colds will become rare.

Susceptibility to colds is lowered resistance to colds and lowered resistance is often a product of emotional stress. Since emotional stress can be successfully alleviated through hypnotism, colds can be successfully alleviated through hypnotism.

Other respiratory aliments such as breathing difficulty, cough, and asthma can be more successfully treated from the point of view of symptom removal. Dramatic disappearance of asthma, after years of suffering, has often occurred in just a few hypnosis sessions much to the amazement of the hypnologists and physicians involved. This amazement stems from the fact that asthma is recognized by many authorities to have psychosomatic aspects. A common characteristic is emotional dependency, threats to which cause extreme anxiety. Yet even without any ventilation of these emotions in psychotherapy or hypnotherapy, rapid cures are possible. This might be so because the once acute dependency has evolved into a habit rather than a functional need and thus is doffed more easily. However, the more common hypnosis treatment for asthma is less dramatic, as the following case history reveals.

A young girl, of junior high school age, was referred to the author by her pediatrician. She was having five to seven asthmatic attacks a day. She had lost weight and her school work had suffered. During the attacks she had to hold on to something to remain erect. Her shoulders were hunched as she fought raspily for every breath.

During the first interview she was asked to write down the time, date, and circumstances of each attack as they would occur in the days that followed and to score each one in intensity—I for a major attack, II for a medium attack, III for a minor attack. When she returned a few days later, the record had been conscientiously kept but it revealed no clue except that there appeared to be some emotional involvement in an activity at the time of many attacks, such as participation in a class project, watching television, etc. She did note that a coughing spell always signaled an attack.

At this session, a fairly deep state of hypnosis was readily attained. The suggestion was given that her attacks would come with less frequency and less intensity. "Each attack will be much milder and the time in between attacks will lengthen. In addition, you will cough from time to time without any asthmatic attack." She was asked to continue her record keeping.

In three days she returned. Her attacks were cut in half. Most of them were mild, of II and III intensity. "How do you feel," "Great!" (Fine, no secondary symptoms.) The process was repeated several times. In two weeks she was down to one minor attack a week. In two months, her asthma was over, with only a rare mild reoccurrence such as when her class had "moving up" exercises to junior high school.

There is a probability in this case that the cough served to perpetuate the asthma symptoms. Any nervous cough would place her in a state of expectation of an attack and thus encourage the subconscious to produce it. This linkage was broken through instant deconditioning in hypnosis.

Hypnotism and Heart Conditions

Persons with heart conditions are anxious, tense individuals. If their anxiety and tension did not cause the heart trouble, certainly the heart trouble has caused them a measure of anxiety and tension. Usually it is an endless cycle with anxiety spawning health conditions that cause more anxiety. The cycle has been broken quickly with hypnotism.

"My heart is bad. I am aware of my heart. I am afraid when it beats fast. I will not do anything to make it beat fast. I expect pain and feel terror at its approach. I dare not drive a car too far from home. I will not do anything that I do not know ahead of time is safe."

These are the innermost thoughts of a heart patient. But are they also hypnotic suggestions? Indeed they are. They are suggestions given by the patient to himself, rather than by the hypnologist. The hypnologist's job is to get the patient to agree to the unreasonableness of his own fear-some premises and then to accept hypnosis as a means to undo what could otherwise be his undoing.

What suggestions are used by the hypnologist to break the anxiety cycle? Each may put them in his own words, but the essence would be: "You are now thoroughly re-laxed. You can repeat this deep state of blissful relaxation at will. You visualize the perfect heart and hear its regular beat. It is your heart. You are confident that your new relaxed attitude makes it possible for you to lead a normal everyday life."

Each person's temperament is considered in the framing of suggestions. For instance, if inhibited rage is the cause of hypertension, suggestions might be directed at under-standing and tolerance or at an innocuous mode of ex-pressing or releasing anger. To develop the "perfect heart" suggestion and permit its translation by the subject into real life imagery, it is helpful to exhibit a medical draw-ing or model and to back the regular beat with a metro-nome set to the subject's normal pulse. This visual imagery is one of the keys to successful suggestion and the ways in which it is used will be discussed in detail in later chapters.

Emotional tension has been shown by recent studies to raise the level of serum cholesterol in the blood by a significant amount in just an hour's time. An increase in the free fatty acids associated with coronary disease has been noted to correspond with increased anger and fear. Thus the link between mind and body is broad, visible, and direct in cardiovascular health problems, an ideal situation for the successful use of hypnotism.

Heart regulating mechanisms are located in the cortex of the brain. Working through the hypothalamus these mechanisms control the rate of the rhythm. Excitement steps up the rate. Pain depresses it. The imagination, when directed at exciting events, will step up the rate just as if the events were real. A person who is afraid of public speaking can increase his own heartbeat by imagining he is about to appear on a stage.

By hypnotically inducing serenity the physiological causes of heart trouble are reached just about as surely as are the emotional causes. Cases have been reported of cardiac output increased through hypnotic suggestions. Palpitations have been controlled, functional chest pains relieved. Electrocardiograms bear witness to dramatic results. And heart patients enjoy these results as they live out their normal span of years.

The Amazing Placebo

For centuries doctors have been prescribing a small pill for a wide variety of ailments varying from heart trouble to nervous tic. This small pill seems to work in a remarkable number of cases. Miracle drug? No, sugar, salt, or bicarbonate of soda, or none of these, or all three. The pill is called a placebo. It is defined in a standard dictionary as "any harmless substance, as bread pills, given to humor a patient rather than as a remedy."

Perhaps the word "humor" has been used to avoid a lengthy explanation of faith healing and its relationship to hypnotism and symptom removal. For the placebo works its miracle healings by suggestion. The patient does not know that he is being given a sugar pill. He has faith in the doctor. The doctor writes out a prescription which he confidently asserts will help the patient. The patient goes to a pharmacy and the prescription is filled. The little white tablets come in a small vial. "Take one every four hours" it says on the label along with the name of the doctor. The pills are taken. They are sugar pills. The ailment vanishes.

How does this happen? The active ingredients of the sugar pill are actually confidence, belief, and expectation. Obviously, if the patient knows the innocuous nature of the pill, nothing can happen. Even if he has a shred of suspicion that the pills might be a placebo, it will not work. It works because of the unquestioned suggestion that it will work, given by a professional man whose integrity is unshakable. It works because medicines work and this is a "medicine."

If readers now distrust medication prescribed by their physicians because of the placebo practice described here, there is no doubt that all of this medication will be nullified to an extent. Miracle drugs owe part of their success to their reputation and popularity. When that popularity wanes, so does their effectiveness. Sometimes this is attributed to the body's building up a "resistance" or "tolerance" to the drugs. There is certainly plenty of evidence for this. But there is also plenty of evidence for the power of suggestion in healing.

How much does confidence, belief, and expectation have to do with effective drug therapy? There may be a way to find out by measuring the results of usual dispensation by white-coated, stethoscoped physicians against the results of a control group of prisoners who have volunteered to submit to experimental "therapy," devoid of confidence, belief, and expectation. But such a test has not been made to our knowledge.

Mesmer knew that imagination and conviction were essential elements in his "cures." Those who succeeded him encouraged their contemporaries to capitalize on the curative effects of faith and conviction. But magic and superstition were on their way out. Faith healing was now for the church. And at Lourdes, where expectations ran high, miracles of healing continued to be the order of the day.

When one knows the miracle of the placebo, one can better understand the miracle of suggestion. It is literally the power of life and death. The suggestion of cure can cure. The suggestion of incurability can kill. There is hardly a physician who does not know that induced fright can kill. Surgeons have known many a patient faced with a routine operation who expected to die on the operating table and did. The danger of the negative suggestion is as real a danger as the germ, the virus, and the poison. Every person is receptive to suggestions. There is no immunity.

Hypnotism offers a powerful antidote to negative suggestions. It permits the power of suggestibility to be opened so that positive suggestions can be injected into the subconscious where they may activate recovery forces and permit latent good health to be robustly expressed.

Hypnotism Knows No Bodily Bounds

To say that there is a part of the body that cannot be helped by hypnotism is to invite challenge. Nearsighted and farsighted eyes have been helped. Deafness has been corrected. A boy with stubborn nosebleeds is hypnotized and the blood coagulates on command. Warts fall off the feet of a sixteen-year-old girl within a few days of the suggestion. One by one allergies are removed from the most lengthy list, many by just a single suggestion, never to return.

People with diabetes, colitis, even cancer, have been benefited through hypnotism. If hypnotism cannot be used to remove a disease symptom, it can be used at least to ease its pain, decrease its shocks, and improve the patient's ability to live with it.

Hypnotherapy is being used for diabetics. The personality factors involved in this disease have long been recognized. Posthypnotic suggestions are aimed at changing both dietary habits and emotional habits. Sweets and starches go down the drain along with anxieties and frustrations. As a result, the quantity of insulin needed to keep urine sugar-free is reduced, sexual impotency and the inability to resist infection (common symptoms with diabetics) are corrected, and the frequency of ketosis attacks is lessened. One study showed that if a hypnotized person is given a concentrated solution of sugar water to drink and told it is distilled water, his blood sugar does not increase but may even sharply drop. What a field for exploration by the biochemists!

Chronic ulcerative colitis is acknowledged to be a by-product of severe psychic strain. It is a very serious, life-threatening condition. After it has taken hold awhile, the inner lining of the bowel looks as if sharp fingernails have scraped away areas of the soft tissue. Eventually an ileostomy is recommended. This is an operation in which a hole is cut in the abdominal wall to act as a new path for excretion and the colon is removed. The result can be very distressing, and there are clubs where people with these operations meet to cheer each other up and swap ideas on how to cope socially with the situation.

In cancer, the all-important "will to live" can be reinforced in hypnosis. The records show how one man, told of the prognosis of less than six months to live, was given posthypnotic suggestions for pain reduction and for the improvement of his morale. He became very optimistic as well as religious, praying every day. He began to gain weight and was soon free of all cancer symptoms. Years later the patient was still in good health. This is not to suggest that all cancer patients can be cured. But there is not a shadow of a doubt that as the image of cancer is changed from one of inevitable death to one of probable survival, the management of that disease will change for the better. Hypnotism is a way of altering that image now, and of removing it as a dead weight on the will to live and the forces of recovery.

Fortunately, for every person in a sick room, there are ten to fifteen who are working and well. But even among the healthiest of us there are emotional problems that affect our behavior in ways that brings us long days and long nights of quiet desperation. These emotions may one day lead us to the sick room, but before that, they can also lead us to the court room, prison, divorce, seclusion, and a variety of living deaths. Here, too, hypnotism can be a valuable aid to health.

6

Uses of Hypnotism
for Emotional Health

"I am afraid." How seldom these words are spoken, but how often felt. Fear is an emotion we keep to ourselves because it is usually something we are not proud of. We may not even know we have it. "I am afraid" may hardly ever be voiced aloud, but it is voiced silently and it echoes and reechoes in the long mental corridors of the subconscious.

Millions on this earth live in fear of their life or in fear of starvation. These are the basic fears that are ignited by the will to survive. They are the fears people *must* fear—fears that gird them to take action to avert danger or to obtain food. They are healthy fears. They prolong life.

Others live in fears that arise not out of war and famine but out of dependence, security, attachment, greed, prestige, authority, guilt, rejection, prejudice, loneliness, distrust, taboos, sex, responsibility, and an almost endless torrent of anxiety-causing elements of man's society. They are unhealthy fears. They shorten life.

The first kind of fear—the healthy fear of danger or famine—drives people together. They unite in self-defense or to dam rivers and irrigate the land. They exhort themselves and others to be brave. They flex their muscles and their willpower. The second kind of fear—the unhealthy fear that arises from modern society—drives people apart. The individual is alone in his fear. He disguises it and builds defenses around it. If exposed, his fear does not respond to exhortations of courage. If anything, such exhortations only send it burrowing deeper into these disguises and defenses where it erodes away at personality, behavior, health, and happiness.

Fear is at the root of insomnia and alcoholism. It drives people to obesity, excessive smoking, even drug addiction. It makes them accident prone. It causes lawlessness. It breaks friendships and marriages. It evaporates personal savings, overflows hospitals, and fills cemeteries. Add frustration and you have a pair of emotional culprits that can be blamed for ninety percent or more of man's unhappiness.

The only known antidote to fear is confidence. It can be a religious confidence or a philosophical confidence or just plain self-confidence. In a way, both a religious belief in God and a philosophical understanding of the universe lead to self-confidence. So all confidence is self-confidence, and self-confidence wipes out fear.

A person who is suffering from fear may not be aware that he is. All he knows is his troubles. Tell him they are due to basic insecurity and you get a blank stare or the cold shoulder. If his fear was in his conscious mind, instead of lurking deep in his subconscious, you might have a good chance of reasoning with him and eventually talking him out of it and talking him into an attitude of optimism and assuredness. But because his fear is below the level of awareness, it cannot be reached by reason. Longer tools are needed—tools like psychotherapy and hypnotherapy.

Identifying Fear Through Hypnoanalysis

Hypnotism can be used to identify a fear and then to expose it to the white-hot light of logical scrutiny; or it can be used as in physical health, to remove the symptoms of that fear directly. We will examine both approaches, starting with fear identification through a probing of the subconscious by many of the unusual techniques made possible when the subject is in a state of hypnosis.

If you were to have a season's pass to the hypnologist's keyhole, you would see him in action assisting patients to correct many habits and failings. In some cases, where hypnoanalysis was being used, he might be working with a psychiatrist; in other cases, a psychologist might be attending, or a physician. In most cases he would be working alone, aiding the patient to attack a particular problem such as smoking, obesity, stammering, alcoholism, or the like.

As you observe, an overall pattern would emerge. First, the pre-induction talks that set the subject's mind at rest and that gain his or her permission. Next, the trance induction procedure involving several techinques, but all of them aimed at capturing and misdirecting the attention and relaxing the body. Then comes the period of questions, probing and suggesting, differing with the nature of the problem and the personality of the subject, but all aimed at getting to the roots of the fear even if those roots occurred in infancy. Finally, the emergence—a fast, happy moment with the subject expressing relief from burden, and revitalized with the hope of a new future.

The most engrossing part of the procedure to witness is the analyzing and suggesting while in deep hypnosis. Games of cat and mouse and tug of war are quite common as the hypnologist gets closer to the nest of the problem and the subconscious engages in diversionary tactics.

Here the hypnologist must bring all of his devices to bear on the problem. These include such techniques as automatic writing, hypnodrama, mirror and crystal gazing, regression, and hypnotic drawing.

A salesman for a food company has failing eyesight. He is thirty-eight. The condition has worsened since his father's death three years ago. He has gone to a psychiatrist, but quit after four visits. His opthalmologist cannot find the physiological factor causing the problem but prescribes glasses increasingly strong according to the man's growing needs, finally suggesting that hypnotism be tried. (The opthalmologist had had excellent results with a previous referral, a case of inability to wear contact lenses.) The man agrees to hypnotism grudgingly. The hypnologist's first task is to determine if the man can see without his glasses while in hypnosis. If he can, then further hypnotherapy is indicated.

It takes a number of sessions to reach a deep enough trance state so that the subject can open his eyes (sans glasses) and not disturb the state. Once this stage is reached, a slate is placed before him and the number 103 is written on it. "Now when you open your eyes slowly you will see a blackboard in front of you with a number on it. Do not speak and disturb your trance. Remember the number and tell it to me later." He is awakened. Yes, he saw a number, but he cannot remember it.

The hypnologist senses subconscious resistance. He tries again. This time he writes number 7. "When you open your eyes slowly you will see a number. You will write what you see on this piece of paper." The eyes open. The hand writes. It is number 7. He is awakened. "Did you remember a number this time?" He did not. The hypnologist takes the paper with the 7 on it and folds it up. He is not ready yet to shock the subject with the knowledge that he can see without glasses. First, there is work to do.

At the next session the man goes quickly into a deep trance. This time there is no blackboard work—just conversation.

Hypnologist: Are you very comfortable and relaxed? If so, raise your right hand. (Patient raises hand.) Good. Now I want you to turn back time, just as if it were pages in a book. Turn the page and it is a month ago. A few more pages and it is six months ago. Keep turning back time. Let us go back to three years ago when you first noticed that you needed stronger glasses. You are now back to when you were thirty-five years old. You feel the same. Are you any lighter in weight?

Patient: Yes, I weigh a few pounds less.

Hypnologist: You are wearing the same glasses that you did for a number of years. What do they look like?

Patient: The lenses are thinner. The frames are black.

Hypnologist: What happened around the time that your eyes started to blur with those glasses?

Patient: Nothing.

Hypnologist: Isn't there some major event in your life this year?

Patient: No.

Hypnologist: Isn't this the year your father died?

Patient: I suppose so.

Hypnologist: Do you feel there is any connection between the death of your father and the deterioration of your eyesight?

Patient: No.

Hypnologist: I want you to relax more deeply and as you relax you will feel as if you have no control of your arms. They will feel as if they have a life of their own and are able to raise and lower themselves. If there is a connection between your poor sight and you father's death, your right hand will rise. If there is no connection, your left hand will rise. You may or may not be aware of the movements of your hand. Is there or is there not a connection between your poor sight and your father's death? (Patient raises right hand.) Is one of your hands rising?

Patient: No. (Right hand continues to rise.)

Hypnologist: Now you may return to the present. Just turn the pages of the book back again to the present day. Have you turned time back to the present?

Patient: Yes.

Hypnologist: Good. Now when I count three you will wake feeling refreshed and well. One, two, three!
How do you feel?

Patient: Fine. How did we do?

Hypnologist: Well, with your permission I would like to meet with you at the psychiatrist's office for our next visit. The two of us working with you for a session or two should turn up some good news for you. Let me tell

you now that there does seem to be some
deep-rooted emotional cause to your eye
condition and it may have something to
do with your father's passing. Now you
should be happy to hear this because it
means that the process can be probably
reversed with the help of your psychiatrist, and your good eyesight restored.
Are you willing?

Patient: All right.

"Are you willing?" It was a crucial question. Poor eyesight is his defense, at least it was three years ago. Is he
ready to be defenseless now? The hypnologist could not
assume that he was. In fact, everything had pointed to
his being unready. He had clung tenaciously to the as-
sertion that there was no connection with his father's
death, even in deep hypnosis. Only with dissociating hand
levitation with his subconscious defense mechanism had
it been possible to get admission. Now one had to tread
carefully. "Are you willing to have your eyesight restored?" The answer was "All right." Had the question
been worded "Are you willing to return to the psychiatrist for further analysis?" the answer may have been
different.

The next session is conducted similarly with the psychiatrist present. The pages of time are once more turned
back. The hands are once more given a "life of their
own."

Psychiatrist: When you realized that your father was
going to die, did the thought frighten you
in any way? Your right hand will raise if
the answer is yes, left hand if no. (Patient
raises left hand.) Were you afraid that you
would have no one to turn to if financial
problems arose? (Patient raises left hand.)
Were you afraid of more responsibility
after he was gone? (Patient raises left
hand.) Were you afraid that your mother
would live with you and in some way affect
your home life? (Patient raises left hand.)

At this point the psychiatrist and hypnologist retire to a far corner of the room to confer quietly. It is decided that a different technique will be tried.

Psychiatrist: I am placing a pad and pencil in your hands. They are free to draw whatever they wish to draw. They will draw for me, if I ask them to. Let's see how well your right hand draws a sun. (Patient draws a circle with a cloud or two.) Good: Now I want you to draw a picture of what frightened you when you learned that your father was dying. (Patient begins to draw.)

After the patient has finished drawing, the psychiatrist retrieves the paper and retires once more to the corner with the hypnologist. Together they examine it. It is obviously a body in a coffin. The psychiatrist nods. The fear has been identified. It is a common one. He returns to the questioning.

Psychiatrist: Thank you, hands, for the drawing. Now I have another question. Remember, right for yes, left for no. Are you afraid of viewing a dead person? (Patient raises right hand.) Did you feel that there was no way to avoid this at the funeral, considering it was your father? (Patient raises right hand.) And is this the basic reason that your eyesight was affected? (Again, the right hand.)

The session is ended. The problem has been solved. The subject is scheduled for another session in a few days. Meanwhile the psychiatrist and hypnologist consult on procedure for therapy. The fear is clearly identified; it is the fear of seeing a corpse. No need to delve into the reasons for it. The problem does not arise that often. The next step is to bring it out of the subconscious into the conscious mind where the subject can evaluate it, see it for what it is, and decide to reject it.

This is accomplished at the next and final session. The psychiatrist consults with the patient first. He explains that due to subconscious fears, his eyes have been affected by the death of his father. If he wants to have his good eyesight restored, he must face up to that fact.

They discuss death, embalming, burial. Ancient rituals are described by the psychiatrist. There is no reason why he probably will ever have to view a corpse, but even if he did, he could turn away, or close his eyes. The hypnologist can help him not see a corpse should he ever be confronted by one. Would he be willing to exchange good sight, full time, for temporary bad sight when such a situation arose? The bargain is made. The case history ends at the next session with two posthypnotic suggestions: "Your eyes will not see a corpse if there is ever one in your presence in the future" and "Your eyesight is now fully restored. Your glasses are off. You can see perfectly."

This case history involved the use of three techniques: regression, automatic writing, and hypnotic drawing. It accomplished in three weeks what might otherwise have required months of fifty-minute psychoanalytic sessions. Identify the source of emotional problems—the fears and the frustrations—and you are on the way to getting rid of them. Most of them cannot stand the conscious light of day.

Hypnotism and Obesity

Fears and frustrations do not always puncture health or behavior in a definitive or dramatic way. We all have them, mildly or intensely; and we all have their effects, mild or intense. These effects may never be observed. Or, if observed, they may never be a problem. Who cares about the emotional causes behind a propensity for dropping dishes? You live with it.

Some mild effects of a mild problem may have a way of adding up. Cumulative effects of overeating, even if only an ounce a week, can produce an overweight person in ten years with enough excess poundage to cost ten years off that person's life expectancy. A pack of cigarettes a day can, in ten years, put a person in line for serious trouble, according to cancer research.

Often the mild emotional causes that started us smoking, or initiated the gourmand eating, have long since disappeared; but the behavior remains as an entrenched habit. Will power can be successful, but more likely the

psychological law of "reverse effect" prevails: the harder
you try the more likely you will fail.

Clinical hypnologists are gaining reputations as habit
breakers. They are successful where pills, diets, exercise,
steam, and massage fail. What is more, they can teach
people the art of self-hypnosis as a convenient and useful
habit-breaking tool to have around the house. Step-by-
step procedures on how to use this tool are in the next
chapter. There all stops are off; you may embark on
self-hypnotism safely by following the directions given.
But first let us examine the hypnologist's own procedure
for diverting eating habits from fattening sweets and
starches to the thinning proteins. It too is a step-by-step
procedure:

Step One

The subject confers on his weight loss goals with the
hypnologist, who then discusses with the physician any
possible glandular imbalance or other physical problems
that need to be taken into consideration. A progress
chart is prepared. The fattening nature of sugars and
starches is discussed. The subject agrees that a shift in
his eating habits toward proteins would be beneficial. He
is asked to keep a precise record of his intake over the
next few days. Initial suggestibility tests are given.

Step Two

The food intake record is examined. The carbohydrate
total is analyzed for all three daily meals and in between
snacks. A list of protein foods such as meat, fish, poultry,
eggs, and cheese is prepared. It is called the "Green" or
"Go" list. A list of fruits and vegetables is prepared giving
them in order of their carbohydrate content. This is the
"Yellow" or "Caution" list. Breads, potatoes, cake, cereals,
pasta, and other carbohydrate-heavy foods form the "Red"
or "Stop" list. The subject *agrees* to all the items placed
on their respective lists. Then initial induction tests are
made. A light trance is induced.

Step Three

The subject is now ready for deeper stages of hypnosis.
When a satisfactory stage is reached, suggestions are given
that all foods on the "Go" list are delicious, tempting,
satisfying, and nourishing, and no hunger will be experienced except for these foods.

Step Four

Step Three is repeated and the suggestions are strengthened. If there are still any "Stop" foods being craved, special attention is given to these. The subject is asked what has ever made him nauseous. He is then given the suggestion that these "Stop" foods will make him feel the same way; and he will no longer have any appetite for them.

Step Five

The weight loss is checked. If it is not proceeding at the normal rate of four percent of total weight per month, suggestions are given that smaller portions will produce the same satisfying fullness as larger ones. As a further deterrent to hunger pangs the following technique is occasionally used: "Take your right hand off your lap and place it in an imaginary bowl of warm water. Now hot water is being added to the bowl just as if it was a hot bath. Now you take your hand and transfer it to your stomach. The heat feels good. It is a satisfying feeling just as if you had eaten a meal. Whenever you still feel hungry after you have eaten, you will place your hand on your stomach and this false hunger will give way to a comfortable feeling."

Hypnotism has been used successfully by the author in hundreds of obesity cases. Often these cases were those where other methods had failed. Yet there has been an over eighty percent success record. Patients lose all desire for foods that created the obesity. They gravitate naturally to the right foods. They have no anxiety and guilt feelings about a diet. They need exert no will power. They do not easily revert to their former bad eating habits. They stay slim. Other hypnologists and psychiatrists and psychologists who use hypnotism are having equal success. The method deserves more widespread application.

Hypnotism's Success with Alcoholism

The type of symptom removal used in obesity cases is also applicable in cases of alcoholism; but since the subject may be unable to drink at all or to substitute anything in alcohol's place (as proteins for carbohydrates in the case of obesity), it is usually necessary to give positive suggestions that will help the subject to cope with problems that are at the root of the excessive drinking.

Here is a symptom removal procedure that is commonly applied to alcoholism:

Step One

At the initial interview, the hypnologist attempts to learn about the subject's problems, home life, etc. It is helpful to have other members of the family included at this stage as an alcoholic has a tendency to hold back in projecting the whole picture. The hypnologist makes a point of learning what food or medicine is objectionable to the subject. This information will be used in the next step. Susceptibility tests are given and an optimum induction procedure is determined.

Step Two

This step depends on the depth of the hypnosis. For very deep stages, the taste of liquor can be made revolting. "Anytime in the future that you taste liquor in any form whatsoever, this taste will be the taste of (insert objectionable taste ascertained in Step One)." The hypnologist then asks the subject to visualize this actually happening and to act out the scene. It is possible that the subject will vomit. If there is not even a gagging reflex, the state is not deep enough.

For a lesser stage, time distortion can be used. "From now on, any very small quantity of liquor in any form will produce the same sick feeling that you have experienced from larger amounts." Again the subject is asked to enact the scene.

For a still lighter stage of hypnosis, the following suggestion is effective: "You no longer need liquor to improve your self-confidence. You can be strong, sociable, and efficient without it."

All three types of approaches are then reinforced with confidence-producing suggestions. Also, the subject is asked to visualize two paths. On the left path is a life of drink. It leads to family problems, health problems, and financial disaster. On the right path is life without liquor. It is a happy, healthy, and prosperous life. The subject visualizes himself choosing the right-hand path.

Step Three

Step Two is repeated every day or two for ten days to two weeks. After that, sessions should not be necessary more often than once every two weeks. When good results are confirmed over a period of months, then only one reinforcement session every six months will suffice.

Hypnologists have found that in the treatment of alcoholics, the attitude must be one of tolerance and non-condemnation. Also, the subject must be highly motivated. Treatment of subjects who are there only because they are trying to keep peace in the family has a poor prognosis. Group hypnosis is often successful. There may even be elements of this in Alcoholics Anonymous where the individual is spurred by the competitive situation and supported by others who understand him.

Often, autohypnosis can be taught to subjects so that they can provide their own periodic reinforcement to original sessions.

Some success has also been recorded using the symptom substitution technique where a food or drink is substituted for liquor. "Every time you want a drink of liquor, you will reach for a (peppermint, glass of milk, malted milk tablet) and it will give you full satisfaction and pleasure. You will feel relaxed."

Ending Drug Addiction

Can drug addiction be ended through hypnotism? The answer is an emphatic yes. However this is another of the areas where little if any experimentation under controlled conditions is being conducted. Many capable practitioners in the field have had excellent results. But there is need for further research. Very little medical literature is available on the subject. Certainly the dismal record of the other methods should dictate a thorough trial of hypnotism.

Drug addiction is complicated by withdrawal symptoms. For this reason it is advisable to conduct the hypnotherapy while the subject is at a hospital, nursing home, or similar institution. Suggestions are basically the same as for alcoholics but to these are added suggestions to reduce the agony caused by withdrawal. Here is an actual case history:

A husband and wife were both addicts. Although in their early thirties, they were very successful business people and had worked very hard. They owned a chain of thirty or forty shoe stores. His friends had introduced him to drugs. He in turn introduced drugs to his wife. Soon the cost of the drugs, coupled with their inattention to business, had depleted their income. The chain was on the verge of bankruptcy. Separate corporations were formed and some of the stores did fail.

The wife was the first to be treated. She agreed to enter a private convalescent home. She was hypnotized on the first day and left in the fairly deep state that she was able to attain. Her nurse was taught to give the proper post-hypnotic suggestions every few hours that would continue this deep stage. On the first day suggestions were given that she would have amnesia during the time of her withdrawal symptoms and would not be aware of them. Furthermore she would no longer have any further desire for drugs and in fact would detest them.

She went through the agonies of withdrawal but was never aware of them. She was awakened after seven days. She said she felt calm and relieved. Further sessions were held to strengthen the repulsion and increase self-confidence. She has remained off drugs for over a year to the present writing.

Her husband was a more difficult subject. His habit appeared to be more under control. He did not seem to be as "hooked." He was not institutionalized. Instead, he chose to take very heavy medication to handle his withdrawal symptoms. This medication was reinforced by hypnosis sessions three times a week wherein he was induced to experience withdrawal symptoms and shown how easy it was for him to handle them. "You feel the trembling in your legs beginning. You are aware of it. It distresses you. It becomes more severe. But nevertheless you are able to cope with it and see it through." In such a session, the subject is given the opportunity to terminate on his own. "If you wish to end the session, raise your right hand."

It took longer—three months, but the husband, too, was rid of his habit and also stayed rid of it to the present writing.

A deep state of hypnosis permits a suggestion that the pains of withdrawal will not be felt. A lesser stage dictates a suggestion that they will be only slightly felt with lessened time and intensity (similar to those given the mother about labor pains). These suggestions are reinforced with "Others have done it. You can too."

The dramatic effectiveness of hypnosis in case histories such as this certainly warrants the establishment of a hypnosis center for drug addiction wherein better and better hypnotic techniques can be perfected and turned against this growing social threat.

How to Stop Smoking with Hypnotism

Two methods have had a good measure of success in breaking the smoking habit. One builds up the disgust and motivation and results in immediate stoppage. The other uses time distortion to increase the interval between cigarettes so that a gradual tapering off results.

In the first method, the subject is asked to recall some of the disagreeable aftereffects of excessive smoking. Then in hypnosis, his own words are thrown back to him. "Remember that dark brown taste in your mouth, the breathing difficulty you have? Cigarettes will continuously cause this and will always taste harsh to you." Also thrown back at him are the reasons for his requesting help. "You have felt this fear of lung cancer. You know you will continue to have this fear as long as you smoke." One session is usually enough to bring about an immediate cessation. The subject, if asked to light up, will refuse, saying he has no desire. If he does light up again later, the hypnologist will see him again every three days for two or three weeks. If the complete stop does not come in two more weeks, sessions are not likely to be successful.

In the second method—tapering off—the subject's average daily consumption is divided by his waking hours to determine the approximate time between lights. For instance, forty cigarettes a day means about two and a half cigarettes per hour. The suggestion is given that there will be a longer and longer interval in between cigarettes. In this way, the intervals can be extended to one hour, then two, etc.

Aversion can be built up by associating cigarette taste and odor with other repulsive materials as was done for alcohol. Or, stale cigarettes can be accumulated and sniffed as an aid to such suggestions.

Sometimes a symptom substitute is required to bridge the gap. Hard candies, chewing gum, or dummy chocolate cigarettes are useful. Antihistamines are useful in controlling "withdrawal" symptoms. Of course, the need for relaxing the tension underlying the cause of chain smoking must be recognized. Positive suggestions for this are given by hypnologists in line with those described for self-betterment in the next chapter.

Relief for Insomniacs

Insomnia is self-consciousness about sleep. The good sleeper does not need to try to sleep. It just happens. The insomniac tries like mad and it never happens—until he gives up in the wee hours.

Gradually the insomniac builds up the cycle. In addition to the original concerns and anxieties that kept him awake, he now worries what staying awake will do to his health and energy. Now he is worse off than ever.

Bet a good sleeper a million dollars that he cannot fall asleep in five minutes, and he won't. He may have last night and the night before, but he won't tonight. The insomniac is besieged and beset by fearful thoughts, troubled thoughts, anxious thoughts, worried thoughts, all amplified in the quiet and dark of night.

One attractive divorcee, about forty, took so many pills to help her to sleep that she was too groggy to go to work most mornings. When she came to the author she was at her wit's end. She could not remember the last time she had had a good night's sleep.

When suggestions were given to relax, she seemed to fidget and become all the more nervous, commenting that "It's not working." She seemed to have an almost defiant attitude. So a technique was used to permit her defiance to work for her instead of against her. She was asked to look at the light fixture on the ceiling. "The more you try to stay awake the less able you will be to do so. Keep your eyes wide open. Keep staring intently."

Gradually her eyes began to moisten. She fought to keep them open. "Harder, harder. But you will not be able to stay awake." In a few minutes she succumbed. Her eyes closed. She relaxed physically. Then suggestions were given: "At night you will make no attempt to sleep, but instead you will do everything you can to stay awake— walk around, watch television. The more you try to stay awake, the quicker you will fall asleep." After the third session she reported that fifteen years of insomnia had ended for her. A year later she came back for reverse treatment: she was going to bed too early and sleeping too late.

There are many techniques for breaking the "try to sleep" habit. One effective posthypnotic suggestion is "In a few moments I am going to awaken you. Then I will count backward from ten to one and you will find yourself slipping back to sleep." The hypnologist then awakens the subject who is asked to look at an object on the wall. The hypnologist then counts backward synchronizing the numbers with each breath the subject takes and noting at what number the eyes close. With the subject back in a trance, the next suggestion given is that the same thing will happen again, but this time "Your eyes will close at number five (which they did before) and you will go into an even deeper sleep than before." This happens just as predicted. Now, for the final suggestion. "At home you will count backward. One number every time you inhale, relaxing as you exhale. You will imagine yourself in this office, looking at this object just as you did. You will fall asleep at that same number, just as you did."

Another successful technique is the progressive relaxation which will be taught for self-use in the next chapter. The hypnologist usually guides the subject through it and then gives the posthypnotic suggestion that the relaxation when practiced at home will be as effective as if the subject was in the hypnologist's office.

But the shortage of skilled hypnologists disappears in the next chapter. The reader becomes his own hypnologist and discovers techniques that can raise him out of ruts of unhappiness or failure and elevate him to new heights of self-mastery and success.

7

Self-Hypnosis and Self-Betterment

Understanding hypnotism really pays off when its self-use is understood and can be applied to everyday problems at home. We don't go to a medical doctor with every pain and ache. We understand medicine enough for limited self-use—aspirin for an occasional headache and bicarb for occasional stomach distress. Hypnotism can be used at home *on yourself* safely and easily.

If your medicine cabinet contained a bottle labeled "Self-Hypnosis," some of the symptoms that it would help might be listed as blues, nervous fatigue, fears, guilt, bad temper, personality defects, and tension. It might also state "Often helpful when used for insomnia, alcoholism, smoking, and other unwanted habits." Can you imagine a traveling tonic hawker making such claims for his bottled products a century ago? He would probably add that it cured warts. And he'd be right! His product was successful as a panacea only by dint of his own suggestion. Inside the bottle was probably an innocent placebo. What he was really selling was the cura-

105

tive power of conviction and belief. He, too, was selling self-hypnosis.

On the other side of your self-hypnosis bottle the label might spell out shake-well-before-using precautions such as:

1. If symptoms persist see your doctor. (If self-hypnosis does not make dramatic changes the first few times it is correctly tried, chances are there are serious and persistent emotional causes at work which it is not advisable for you to confront without professional help.)

2. Stay within prescribed dosages. (Do not use more often than recommended in order to reach a goal faster. Remember that even innocent aspirin can be dangerous if taken in excess.)

3. Follow directions. (Foolish or unwise suggestions can boomerang. Don't give yourself suggestions unless they are reasonable and constructive.)

This is a do-it-yourself chapter. Reading it will provide an introduction to Chapters 11 and 12 in which the hypnologist's techniques and skills in the induction and management of hypnosis are described for understanding but not for use. The following will provide the average reader with step-by-step procedures for administering hypnotherapy to himself for a number of problems. Its use can result in a happier married life, a growing number of friends, a thriving bank account, and a totally new outlook on life.

Relaxation—First Step in Self-Hypnosis

Émile Coué, the French psychologist, wrote a book on self-mastery through conscious autosuggestion early in this century and soon had people everywhere looking into the mirror and saying, "Day by day in every way I am getting better and better." Many of them did get better and better. Many did not. It was probably because they did not believe it would work. It works only for those who say it as if it were true. The "as if" principle is a fundamental one in self-hypnosis. Every thought, image, and suggestion must be "as if" it were true. The fact is, it is true. For no sooner is the thought, image, or suggestion entertained, than it works, automatically. The degree to which it works depends on your own state of relaxation. Everybody is open to suggestion. The advertising industry bears testimony to this. But relaxation opens the pores of suggestibility and brings visualized suggestions straight to the subconscious. You will get to know more about the subconscious as you give it suggestions and watch it carry them out. You will find it to be somewhat childish in many ways. For instance, it will try to protect its current ways. It will send up thoughts to the conscious aimed at deterring you from further effort to eliminate a fear or phobia or some other attitude that it might need as a defense. You will find yourself saying, "Oh, this won't work, no use trying," or "I'm too busy to do it now."

It will also be very literal. Suggest to yourself, "I am going to take just a minute to relax very deeply." At the end of sixty seconds, you will find the period over whether you meant it to be or not.

Sigmund Freud divided the subconscious into three parts: the id, the super-ego, and the preconscious. The id is memory and basic instincts, the super-ego is conscience, and the preconscious is the dream world just on the other side of consciousness. Dr. Carl Jung connected the unconscious mind to a universal subconscious which he called the superconscious. More recently Dr. Norbert Wiener, a professor at the Massachusetts Institute of Technology, coined the word cybernetics to describe the subconscious doing its work like an electronic computer with no ability to reason.

No matter what view we take of the subconscious—as a purely mechanical computer, as a spiritual tie to the universe, or as something in between—the most effective way we can reach it for immediate reconditioning is by relaxation. So if you wish to be successful in self-hypnosis, you must learn a relaxation technique similar to one of those used by the hypnologist, one that you find able to use comfortably.

The method used in Chapter 3 under the subheading "A Hypnosis Session Begins" (p. 42) is known as the hand levitation method of inducing deep relaxation and a fairly responsive state of hypnosis. If "I" is substituted for "you," it can be converted into a monologue suitable for your use. You cannot read the words and expect them to work. What you have to do is remember the main thoughts. Then visualize them happening in your mind's eye:

1. You sit comfortably, breathe deeply, and relax every muscle one by one.

2. You watch your left hand. It starts to move. With each breath it lightens.

3. Your hand begins to rise. You know your eyes will close before your hand touches your face. As it touches your face you know you are in a deep state of relaxation.

If you perform this exercise several times just to become adept at it prior to banging away with some life-changing suggestions, be sure to remember that there is a Step 4 and a Step 5. Step 4 is visualizing the changes that you wish to have take place; and Step 5 is terminating the session with a "wide awake, feel fine" suggestion as you count one, two, three.

You may not be ready for the specific suggestions for Step 4 until you read further along in this chapter, but you can practice meanwhile with a suggestion that will help you with each subsequent practice session: "I can visualize my next practice session. I can see myself reaching an even deeper stage quickly and easily."

Then you end the session. You will truly feel wonderful. It is like having your batteries recharged. A nap sometimes leaves you feeling sleepy and dull. Not this relaxation session. It puts energy and briskness into your step and makes you feel younger and ready to tackle whatever lies ahead.

If this method of relaxation does not appeal to you for some reason, there is another method which does not require moving the hand: You fix your gaze on an object, such as a candle or a spot on the ceiling. Then you tell yourself that as you watch the spot your eyelids will become heavier and that your eyes will close. See your eyes closing in your visual imagination. It will be almost impossible to keep them open. They should be closed in two or three minutes. Then see your muscles relaxing. Start with the muscles in your toes and work right up through feet, ankles, legs, thighs, back, shoulders, neck, arms, and face.

A good way to deepen relaxation is to say to yourself that with every breath you take you will go deeper and deeper into a relaxed stage until you reach the count of ten or twenty. Since a picture is worth a thousand words, you might picture yourself going down deeper and deeper in an elevator, floor by floor as your count progresses.

Ask the Subconscious

Time goes fast in this deep state of relaxation. You are completely aware of everything around you, yet you are in a state that might be described as lessened animation. You are not asleep, yet you might slip off into a nap the first time or two that you try it, especially if you are fatigued. You have been in this state before. Movies, religious ceremonies, theater can induce this same stage. Driving along a highway at night can do it. Daydreaming does it.

Many unique opportunities are possible in this state, since you use it only for self-improvement and habit control. For instance, it is possible to question your subconscious mind about matters that concern you. Here is how: Ask your subconscious to select a finger or a hand to signify the answer *yes,* and one to signify the answer *no.* Using these indicators you might find it interesting to ask such questions as "Is Bill the right man for me to marry?" "Should I take the job offered to me by the Smith Company?" "Is the cause of my insomnia a sex problem?"

Since questions can only be answered *yes* and *no,* they must be carefully framed to be devoid of implied answers or double meaning. They should be simple and clear. Should an answer not be forthcoming, try rewording the question so as to break it down into simple components.

Sometimes when a finger rises only partly or both fingers rise, the subconscious is trying to indicate an indeterminate situation where maybe or perhaps is the only possible answer. The finger, in any case, may take a moment or two to react. Wait patiently, making no effort to force the issue.

Another way to "mine" the subconscious for causes and revelations about your behavior and temperament is to use the automatic writing technique described in Chapter 3. Many people have learned automatic writing in one try. Others find that it just does not work for them. Here is a simple way to try:

Place a pad with a heavy backing on your lap. Hold a soft pencil or ballpoint pen in a writing position. Perform your relaxation exercise. Then tell your subconscious to control your hand and to write whatever it wishes to. Then wait. If nothing happens, draw a circle or a square or write your name. Then wait again. Watch your hand expectantly. Feel that it is going to move momentarily, but do not attempt to move it. If it does start to move, watch it as if it was someone else's hand, not your own. Some subjects perform better with their eyes closed. Try it both ways.

The process may take ten or even twenty minutes to begin. The result may look like doodles, or it may be in scrawly handwriting with words run together. The meaning in any case is intriguing. Usually it contains an important truth about yourself or about a problem. It may be literal or symbolic.

Another way to communicate with your subconscious profitably is to ask for answers. Later they will pop into your mind. You have had this experience when you try to remember a name. When you try to remember it, it is like asking your subconscious for the answer. Later it pops up when you least expect it. The same thing will happen with the answers to other problems. You might do this and not get the answer until the next day. But very often, get it you will! You will have an idea. Then you will suddenly recognize it as the answer you asked for.

Then there is the pendulum method. It has become a popular party game. It is less a game, though, than it is a serious method of contacting the inner mind for guidance. A button or other object is tied to the end of a string about ten inches long. The elbow is placed on a table and the string held in the hand so that the button can swing freely. There are now four movements that the pendulum can make: side to side, front to back, circular clockwise, and circular counterclockwise. Give your subconscious whatever code you wish it to follow, such as side-to-side is yes, front to back is no, one circular movement is maybe, another is "no answer possible."

A "no answer possible" can often be interpreted as an unwillingness by the subconscious to divulge information that can lead to the loss of one of its defenses. You saw this happen to the psychiatrist and hypnologist in Chapter

3 where the subconscious refused to acknowledge a casual relationship between the father's death and his own partial blindness.

More likely than not the pendulum will move quite distinctly, swinging back and forth or round and round in response to questions. It is nothing magical, merely another manifestation of how the subconscious controls our movements, health, and habits.

Tell the Subconscious

Asking the subconscious to divulge its secrets is a trickier matter than telling the subconscious to alter behavior. This telling is a gentle process. It is not authoritarian or abrupt. It is permissive, suggestive, and patient. It is done in small, easy-to-take steps. There is no clash or violent change. You nudge yourself into a slightly different direction as a cow noses her calf.

It is symptom control. All the precautions used by the hypnologist in watching for possible secondary symptoms are observed by you. This is easy as you move forward slowly and easily with the reins firmly in your own control.

The previous chapter showed how hypnologists have successfully dealt with cases of excessive drinking, smoking, and eating. You can deal with yourself in the same way. The hypnologist has to conjure up images through the careful use of words. You have an advantage. You can do without words and use ideas and images directly.

Tens of thousands of men and women, young and old, have been taught self-hypnosis by their physicians, psychologists, dentists, and pastoral advisors. Many, many more have learned it themselves by following instructions in books and manuals. It is safe and effective. You have every reason to be confident that the suggestions you give yourself will work.

There are some prerequisites. First, you must thoroughly want the suggestion you give yourself to work. You cannot visualize yourself thin, for instance, if you do not fully believe that it can come to pass. One rather obese young lady was not responding to thinning suggestions. "I just can't see myself thin," she said. The hypnologist asked for a photograph of herself. She brought it in next time. He excused himself for a few minutes and then returned. He held up the picture. She gasped. By masking out parts of the photo, he had made her look thin. She started to cry. At last she could *see herself* thin. It was the turning point. In a few months she *was* thin. Applied to the case of an alcoholic, he must be truly sick of his life and be ready for a change. Otherwise suggestions for a change will fall on a deaf, unreceptive subconscious.

A second prerequisite is that you are deeply relaxed. It pays to practice relaxation exercises for a few days before you attempt to change any habits or personality factors.

A third prerequisite is that you visualize realistically. You must picture yourself carrying out each suggestion. You see yourself eating meat and fish instead of bread and potatoes. You see yourself a better salesman by visualizing yourself going out of the house to attend business courses. You actually see yourself getting up in the morning, showering, breakfasting without having a cigarette. This is the "as if" principle again. You must visualize it as if it were true.

The life you visualize will be your own without an iota of doubt once these prerequisites are met and proper techniques of symptom control are followed.

Let us suppose you are timid about speaking before a number of people. It is impairing your social life and hurting your business career. Do you relax and then visualize yourself the life of the party? Not exactly. It would be too big a step to take. Small steps are more effective and you run less risk of boomerang. In this case, say, you run into a road block by visualizing yourself talking to a large group of people. You start to perspire. Your knees feel weak. You feel all the symptoms that you now feel when you are in front of people.

A first step for the shy public speaker should rather be visualizing himself speaking animatedly and convincingly with one or two near relatives; then he can gradually increase the audience.

One young man who was afraid to speak to a group of people was finding it difficult to get through college. He lived alone with his dog. His first step was to record his voice speaking to his dog. He listened to the recording while in a deep relaxation and visualized himself talking to one or two classmates. Then a few more. Then a whole class. He never made the debating team, but his self-consciousness diminished as the visual exercises began to take hold. He became a happier and more successful student.

To give your subconscious a suggestion against nervous tension is not to merely say, "I will overcome nervous tension." You visualize yourself taking time out for fun and recreation, you see yourself in a less concerned and more confident frame of mind.

To give your subconscious a suggestion to improve confidence in your own abilities is not merely to say, "I will be more self-confident." It is to visualize your personality's strong points in action, to see yourself doing more and more, better and better.

To give your subconscious a suggestion against impotence or frigidity is not merely to say to yourself, "I will be passionate in bed." It is to visualize yourself expressing affection with your loved one, to see yourself free of concern and able to caress and be caressed.

So it is through the art of deep relaxation and "as if" it were true visualizing that you can reprogram your subconscious computer and change your life. You can become a more tolerant and mature person. You can control such runaway emotions as hate, anger, fear, and selfishness. You find out what anxieties or phobias are obstructing your happiness and then visualize them away. You can eliminate feelings of inferiority and substitute complete self-confidence in its place. You can make a greater business success, advance your professional career, dissipate personal antagonisms, improve marital relations, restore vitality and energy, remove depression, overcome insomnia, win friends, influence people, and yes—through better emotional health—increase your life span.

Use Self-Hypnosis to Stop Smoking

The report by the U.S. Surgeon General's Office on smoking and health has triggered countless thousands to try to free themselves from the grip of tobacco. Clinics have been started in many cities to guide would-be non-smokers in the "cure." There have been five-day clinics, two-week clinics, and clinics for those who did not succeed at the first clinic.

These sometimes make use of the "disgust" method,

as with the previously described movie showing an operation for lung cancer. Another way to use this approach would be to visualize the heat and flame of burning tobacco entering your mouth and searing sensitive tissues in your throat and lungs. However, positive methods are preferable to these negative approaches.

Suggestions for self-use are safer when the emphasis is on the positive approach. First, you have to make a decision. You must be ready to give up smoking. You must be thoroughly convinced that smoking can be a killer, that it is an unsafe and undesirable habit. If you are not convinced of this, if you are not ready to smoke your last cigarette, go on to the next chapter and come back to this some other time.

You will keep smoking until you are ready to stop. No clinic, no treatment, not even hypnosis, can break you of a habit against your will. You must have the will to stop before you can stop. Once you decide that the day must come, the day will come without any further will power, through autosuggestion.

When you are ready to say those vital words "I Am Ready," you will drop the habit. There will be no tapering-off period, no gradual withdrawal. One day you will be a smoker. The next day you will be a nonsmoker. Smoking differs from personality changes. No small steps here. So if you say you are ready, better mean it.

You will give a kindly, permissive suggestion to your subconscious, one which it may take the subconscious several days to act on. But act it will. Then one day, soon, you will know when you put down a cigarette that it was your last.

Because of the long ingrained habit that smoking is for most people, it is advisable to avoid the impact of forcefully directed suggestions to stop. Instead, your autosuggestions should be more permissive. You see yourself as a nonsmoker. You are getting closer to the time when you will actually become a nonsmoker. You even give yourself a period of two weeks for this seed to germinate.

Here is a procedure to follow:

1. Review why you want to stop smoking. Write down the reasons. Be completely honest with yourself. Spell them out without subterfuge. Fear of ill health, threat of cancer, danger of a throat operation. Pull no punches.

2. Use your easiest and quickest method of induction into a deep state of relaxation as described earlier.

3. Tell yourself: "I am now relaxed, I can picture in my mind the ill effects if I continue to smoke. I place my hand on my throat. By tightening my fingers gently I begin to get a closed feeling in my throat. I remove my hand. That closed feeling in my throat is one which I will prevent by discontinuing smoking. I can picture myself as a nonsmoker. My food tastes better. I am healthier. I put my hand on my chest. Here, too, tobacco can hurt me. I remove my hand. I am becoming ready to cease smoking. I will soon stop completely, not by will power, not by conscious control, but by the knowledge that I have the inner feeling that I never need smoke again. I will stop smoking in the next two weeks. I will pick a time after a bad cigarette."

4. You close the self-hypnosis session with the usual suggestion for being alert, happy, and full of energy.

Practice the above for several sessions during the period of one week. The mention of two weeks is dropped to one week as the time approaches. This suggestion permits the body to get used to the idea for a brief period before actually acting on it. You cushion the impact and provide an emotional transition period. If during this period, you feel like smoking just as strongly as ever, you have probably used the suggestion as a persuasive factor rather than as an accepted, unquestioned truth. Uncritical acceptance is essential to all hypnosis. It is why so much emphasis is placed on the original decision—its motivation, sincerity, and finality. If truly uncritical acceptance is present, you will feel less desire to smoke. Do not take advantage of this and insert your will. Keep on smoking until you stop without effort.

You will probably have to cope with those notorious withdrawal symptoms that have plagued persons after they drop the cigarette habit. An accelerated use of candy, chewing gum, or increased drinking of coffee are the most common transitional crutches. You might try keeping liberal quantities of healthful fruit juice in home or office.

Withdrawal symptoms will not be as serious a problem with the self-hypnosis method of ending the tobacco habit as it might be in other methods using conscious will. In fact, you can use suggestions in self-hypnosis which will counteract the tension and anxiety that spark those symptoms. These suggestions will work even better than tranquilizers that merely depress the nervous system for a short while and at an eventually prohibitive cost in emotional health.

Suggestions should always be positive. To end nervousness, irritability, tension, you do *not* say, "I will not be nervous, irritable, tense." Instead, you *do* say, "I will be calm, confident, and relaxed." Back up these positive words with some ten-thousand-word pictures—you see yourself participating in your favorite relaxing sport or lolling on the beach. You imagine yourself listening to your favorite music. With some obvious exceptions, music has a tranquilizing effect and could actually be used during a self-hypnosis session to magnify its calming effect.

Soon, you will feel you have always been a nonsmoker. It will be the most natural thing in the world to refuse a cigarette. You will be the beneficiary of better health and sharper senses. You will have done it all yourself.

Conquer Alcohol with Self-Hypnosis

For the average social drinker there is no problem. But for the person who drinks to the point of repeated inebriation, a habit has set in that has foreboding consequences. Psychotherapy seldom succeeds. The combination of group therapy and discipline offered by Alcoholics Anonymous has a comparatively good record of success. Hypnosis is chalking up a promising record of cures and self-hypnosis is not far behind.

Like any excess, there is an emotional cause behind the drinking compulsion. In many, if not all cases, this cause can be uncovered. In few cases can it be removed. Some of the causes of alcoholism are fear, tension, and frustration. Excessive drinking constitutes escape.

Most of these causes are deep-seated. How can one be willing to give up fear or to resign a sense of insecurity? Yet that willingness to relinquish the underlying attitude is an essential prerequisite to a permanent cure.

How then do you proceed under self-hypnosis? The successful formula calls for a gradual attack on the emotions and attitudes that cause excessive drinking. Through suggestion, the risks are pointed out dramatically, and the advantages which accrue from not drinking are clearly and repeatedly emphasized. Uncritical acceptance is obtained regarding a happier and healthier life without alcohol and this is the wedge for successful self-hypnosis. You back this up with suggestions regarding the bad taste of alcoholic beverages. You visualize yourself healthier without them. You see yourself passing up drinks at a party, or limiting yourself to one or two.

One married woman, in her forties, was fast becoming an alcoholic. She decided to try to help herself with self-hypnosis. To start, she used the "disgusting" technique. After the very first session she felt a distinct distaste for the usual before-dinner cocktail. The one-drink-leading-to-another routine never got off the ground. It was the beginning of the end for her bout with alcohol. As she put it, "At first I felt a depressed, left-out feeling. This was not helped at all by my friends who chided me for being antisocial. However, two self-hypnosis sessions a week was enough. I used them to overcome depression with positive suggestions that appealed to my vanity and desire for good health. At the same time I reinforced my newly acquired aversion to alcohol. Today my pattern of drinking is entirely changed. I can have one or two social drinks. Instead of downing them, I nurse them along. I prefer the taste of champagne—an expensive taste but considering what I had gone through, it is a taste well worth having."

The suggestions that helped this woman and many others and which can be used by any excessive drinker are basically: "I don't need it. I can be what I want to be without it. I can taste the ill effects of alcohol. It tastes like the bitter fruit it is. I strive to attain the level of self-mastery and good health that I know I can reach."

The end may not come as quickly or finally as in the above case history. There may be another "humdinger" of a night. Perhaps still another. But as you practice relaxation and suggestion, the forces working for you will one day—or night—spell finis to overindulgence.

Improving Social Relations

A more permissive and gentler approach is apparent in the technique of self-hypnosis to stop smoking and alcoholism than in that of the clinical hypnologist. You do not minister to yourself in as firm or direct a fashion. In this way you skirt conflicts which he would recognize and be able to cope with in his management of your hypnosis, but which you might not be in a position to either see or deal with. Self-hypnosis is thus a weaker sister to hypnosis on these matters and professional help is to be preferred.

The rewards of self-hypnosis lie in the washing away of fear and the building up of self-confidence, in the home, the office, at social functions.

Take the case of a particular nineteen-year-old girl. She was unable to enter a room where there were strangers, even her own family's living room. She could not even go to the bathroom at home, if it meant walking by a doorway where she could be seen by a friend of the family. She stayed in her room. She had been a good high school student, but now she was afraid to look for work.

This girl was taught self-hypnosis. She was then asked to list her assets. She agreed that she had some strong points. She came from a fine family, she was interested in art, she was a good student, she felt that she was loyal to her family and the few she could number among her friends. These assets were to be her building blocks to self-confidence.

The next step for her was to practice relaxation and to visualize these assets at work. She saw herself admired and looked up to. She pictured her art as the topic of conversation. She visualized herself walking up to a friend of her family and shaking hands confidently.

She backed up these images with straight verbal suggestions. "I will be less critical of myself." "The loyalty I possess is a great asset and others will admire me for it." "Other people will enjoy my company."

To an outsider there was no dramatic end to this story. She became an average conversationalist, got an average job. But to her it was release from prison and the opening of new horizons.

The use of self-hypnosis to pull the blinds down over shortcomings is misuse of self-hypnosis. Accept your inferiorities. This professional psychiatric advice deserves to be brought to the popular level of homespun philosophy. You are a poor cook, but you are an excellent artist. Play up the artist in you but don't try to make yourself out to be a better cook than you know yourself to be.

Self-hypnosis has also been used to bring about changes in body shape and contour. It is easy to understand what this simple exercise can do: Stand in front of a full-length mirror. Slowly pull yourself up to your full erect stature—shoulders back, stomach in. Remember this image of yourself. Now proceed to attain your deep state of relaxation. When thoroughly relaxed, see yourself erect as you did in the mirror. See yourself walking in this way with a firm and youthful gait. Then give yourself the usual termination suggestion that you will arise feeling fine at the count of three. One, two, three.

This exercise will work wonders with tired stances, middle-age slump, and sagging shoulders. It can change your whole physical appearance.

It is not as far a step as you might think from this exercise to the exercise used by many young women to enlarge their breasts. Visualizing their bust line as they would like it to be has brought rewards of one to two inches in a remarkably short time. Many beauty courses rely on supplemental autosuggestions to varying degrees. If you do not believe you can increase your radiance and good looks by visualizing yourself as attractive, why not try the opposite? You will find that subconscious opposition to the results of such misuse of the imagination will make it hard for you to do!

Much of the success of spiritual healers and of Christian Science practitioners can be attributed to the power of self-hypnosis. The meditative Yoga exercises, positive thinking, and the self-affirmation of many spiritual disciplines contain strong elements of self-hypnosis.

All of the books that focus on the psychological and psychodynamic laws of self-help and self-improvement can be boiled down to two words: Admire yourself. Self-hypnosis offers the key to their application. With self-hypnosis, attitudes can be reprogrammed from habitual self-depreciation to habitual self-admiration. And the whole world loves a winner.

8

How Hypnotism
Improves Physical Skills

The extraordinary effect that imagination has on the mind
and the body has been clearly demonstrated. How hypnotism and self-hypnotism harness imagination to permit
attainment of physical potential can now be understood
more readily.

Suggestions that remove the lack of self-confidence
that causes social problems can be carried a step further
to suggestions that remove similar self-limiting barriers
that hinder physical performance.

The St. Louis Browns sought the assistance of a hypnologist to raise their sagging batting average more than
twenty years ago. Since then hypnotic conditioning has
been used successfully by basketball players, trackmen,
golfers, bowlers, swimmers, and players, both amateur
and professional, in a long list of sports. Hypnosis sessions are not an integral part of spring training, yet.
Nor have the results been officially or universally recorded,
or scientifically measured. Only case history reports linger
on. But they are dramatic reports of new endurance, new

speeds, and new records. Hypnotism can, however, be abused in this application as in any other. Suggestions that seek to expand physical ability directly are doomed to failure. They can create psychological conflict and anxiety; they may also be physically hazardous.

The Well-Hit Golf Ball

Golfers have been quick to see the part that autosuggestion plays in their game. "Concentrate on staying out of the rough, and that's where your ball will go," says one pro. Another puts it this way: "I visualize the perfect shot and I ignore everything else."

If you were watching a televised bowling tournament recently, you saw one of the country's top pros miss a needed spare by a wide six inches from a lone standing pin. He had all the physical know-how he needed, but somehow he interfered with it. Millions of other players are also beating themselves.

Hypnosis turns off the pressure of consciously knowing the score, feeling the tension, and fearing the outcome. It turns on the subconscious power of rhythm, balance, aim, and timing.

One Sunday golfer who came to the author to improve his game (and his petty cash winnings) had been shooting in the high nineties. He had been playing golf for twenty years and had not improved in the last ten. After several days of instruction in self-hypnosis and three practice sessions in the quiet of his study at home, this man shot an 82 next time out. Now, one year later, he is accustomed to the high seventies.

What happened to improve this man's game? He was an avid reader of golf instruction books. He had not taken lessons from a golf pro recently, but the first ten years that he played he had taken lessons on and off. He felt he knew enough about the game, but it seemed that the harder he tried, the worse he got. And with a dollar a hole at stake, his Sunday foursome was getting costly.

The hypnologist taught him how to relax, how to give himself affirmative suggestions while relaxed, how to visualize the perfect shots.

As a result of these suggestions here is what happens: The player tees off confidently and without anxiety. There is no straining for those extra thirty yards, no furtive glances at the rough borderlines along the fairway, no self-consciousness about the mechanics of his swing, no taking his eye off the ball. His swing is correctly balanced. His timing is perfect. The ball is hit squarely. The drive is a long one and just where he visualized he wanted it.

As science studies how the mind works its wonders, science discovers even more wonders that the mind works. The subconscious mind has the power to imitate the best golf swing we have seen, even if it was seen twenty years ago. Its partner, the conscious mind, has the power to create the optimum theoretical path for the golf ball even if we have never been in that exact "lie" before. Through hypnosis the subconscious mind is instructed to do its best, and the conscious mind is permitted to do its best. Result: the well-hit golf ball.

Hypnotism cannot, however, take someone who has never been out on a golf course before and make a golfer out of him, or turn a bridge player into a tennis player. The person must have learned the rudiments of the game and played at it a good number of times. Also, he should know what an expert at the game looks like, how the game is played when it is played well. Then hypnotism can go to town and bring out the champion in him.

Learning a sport and trying to improve oneself in it makes a person self-conscious. It involves concentrating on oneself. This is a necessary initial procedure because it is the input that conditions the subconscious so that it can then perform the task on command. But the subconscious is an extraordinary pupil. It learns fast. Remember when you first learned how to ride a bicycle? The self-conscious fear of losing your balance takes longer to get rid of than the subconscious ability to keep your balance takes to acquire. When the steadying hand is taken away without the child's knowledge, he rides. The moment he discovers he is soloing, down he goes. Later, the realization that he can ride sinks in and fear subsides along with self-consciousness.

If you are a golfer, right now your subconscious probably plays better golf than you do, maybe by twenty or thirty strokes. It may bowl better than you do by fifty to seventy pins and maybe more. It can probably bat nearly a thousand. All that is needed is to play down that self-conscious deterrent and play up the subconscious propellant.

The hypnologist, through suggestion, reduces self-consciousness. He can also go to work against anxieties, tensions, obsessions, and a score of attitudes and personality traits that work against you. The woman who just *knows* she is not going to be able to negotiate her car into that parking space has her counterpart on the golf course in the woman who faces a water hazard and *knows* that the three-mile-an-hour zephyr wafting against her is a thirty-mile-an-hour gale. Can't you just hear the splash?

The chip-on-the-shoulder business executive who rides his junior assistants all day to release some burden of his libido will be working up a lather on the golf course, you can be sure, either against the foursome up ahead or against his caddy. Can't you just see the slice?

Take a cross section of players on the links and you will find a varied number of typical personality handicaps that keep them slicing and chopping, and putting long, short, and wide. You will find worry warts and gloom-and-doom pitch men. You will find spoil sports and pessimists. You will find them toting personality burdens far heavier than their golf bags, burdens that carry on to the golf course all the way from their office desks and marital beds.

The hypnologist's first step is a sort of emotional surgery. Negative personality traits and habits become ingrained failure mechanisms. They must be cut out and replaced with success mechanisms—the positive assets of confidence and optimism. Some great coaches, like the late Knute Rockne, have the ability to stir a team to new peaks of effort. They are authoritarian figures conducting a type of group hypnosis. They fire the imagination of their players. They build conviction and belief in victory. However, they are not likely to be hanging around a fairway or green when you need them!

The definition of a well-hit ball is one struck squarely with the center of the club face so that its line of flight takes it toward the hole. The good golfer knows that if it is the toe or heel of the club face that hits the ball, a spin is imparted that causes the ball to lose both direction and distance.

The most important visual image that the golfer must hold in his mind's eye is the few inches of swing leading up to impact with the ball, and a few inches of follow-through.

The next most important visual image is that of a perfect swing, somebody else's perfect swing if necessary, but his own if possible.

Champion golfer Gary Player is the first to admit that the difference between an excellent golfer and a champion is just plain unadulterated confidence. Indeed, it is what others might even call overconfidence. For instance, the average confident golfer approaching the green will think to himself that he will chip the ball as close to the cup as he can and then hole out with a single putt. But not Player! He visualizes himself sinking the ball on the chip shot and very often does exactly that.

Finally comes the image of the perfect trajectory. This depends on the lie of the ball and the course. The "pro" studies this from several directions, making wind allowances, and other corrections. His subconscious is then programmed.

These three steps do not require the presence of the hypnologist on the course as caddy or kibitzer. In one or two visits the clinical hypnologist can teach the subject to master relaxation and trigger self-confidence. He can teach the subject to control the visual imagination so that it concentrates before each shot on the three visual images of impact, swing, and trajectory. By post-hypnotic suggestion, the player becomes the agent of the hypnologist and is able to enjoy the benefits miles away when needed.

Hours of Practice in Minutes

Then there is the technique of time distortion. We saw how it was applied to relieve hours of discomfort and make them tolerable minutes. Now we will see how it can give hours of practice in just minutes of imagery.

The hypnologist can ask the golfer to see himself replay the last eighteen holes. He can suggest that it will take only ten minutes, even less, to follow himself around in his mind's eye and see himself hit each ball. He can ask him to observe what he did wrong on those shots that went awry. The golfer will know and he will be able to tell the hypnologist later just what he saw.

Now the hypnologist puts him through some practice

swings. He is asked to visually correct the errors he notices. More pause at the backswing. Right elbow close. He can then practice these swings a hundred times in a few minutes, visually.

Listen to golf pros tell how they prepared themselves for a championship tournament and some will describe these same mental exercises. Yet they may not know anything about hypnosis or self-hypnosis. One pro visualized himself on the green. He viewed himself as a spectator would. He saw himself putt from twenty- and thirty-foot distances. He looked at himself stroke the ball; he saw it roll surely toward the cup; he watched it drop in. He went through this same visual practice with his irons and woods.

Another pro says he visualizes himself actually playing the course. Knowing every hill and trap, he is able to play a round in his imagination. Through time distortion he is able to do it in relatively few minutes.

Of course, the hypnologist can help the golfer with this procedure and through suggestion magnify the time distortion manyfold:

"I want you to picture yourself ready to tee off. Can you do that? Fine. Have you taken a few practice swings? See yourself try this now. Now you are ready to play eighteen holes. As you see yourself stroking in perfect form, you will watch the flight of the ball. When it comes to rest you will be able to see yourself by the ball again immediately, selecting the proper club for your next shot."

Time has been saved by eliminating the walk between strokes. It can be shortened even further with a standard time distortion suggestion to the effect that "You will find that each hour is like a minute."

Practice in any sport can be spoon-fed in this way. Condensed and effective, it has been used for batting, pitching, or fielding; it has helped tennis players with their serves and volley; and it can be applied to basketball, hockey, and other sports.

Tension and Jitters Play Havoc

The relaxation that introduces hypnosis and self-hypnosis is in itself a boon to athletes in competitive sports. Tension is the foe of champions. It is not only the tension

and jitters that come with large stakes and big audiences.
That is bad enough. But there are also the personal tensions, the private crosses borne by individual players.

One baseball player on a major league team had been
hit in the head by a pitched ball. He became plate-shy
and tense. He changed his batting stance so that he could
move away from the plate faster. Of course, his batting
average dropped. He was helped by a psychiatrist using
hypnotism. A posthypnotic suggestion was given that the
chances of such a thing happening ever again were very
remote. He then used imagery to see himself striding up
to the plate in his old confident and relaxed form. The
change was dramatic and his batting average was soon
restored.

A golf celebrity found that his game had been on the
downslide ever since one of his drives struck and injured
a spectator. It took one session of hypnosis, containing
the "remote possibility" suggestion, and relaxation on the
course was once again possible.

Relaxation is perhaps nowhere more necessary for a
winner than in bowling. The average good bowler enjoys
a few strings with a bunch of the fellows and chalks up
a 200 average. Then comes Tuesday night league play.
He goes in there trying. Gone is his normal relaxed delivery. He visualizes his teammates' feelings if he misses
this one. He doesn't realize it, but he has missed already
without the ball ever leaving his hands. Score—182, a
bad night.

Hypnosis permits the bowler to take his relaxed practice
games into the closest of league play finals. Whether self-
induced or assisted by a hypnologist, the state of hypnosis is used to provide posthypnotic suggestions for banning
tension and jitters. This is followed by visual imagery of
the bowler seeing himself bowling with perfectly coordinated delivery. He sees himself in top, natural form. His
rhythm and style are etched in his subconscious. The
images are then stored until the next time he plays. It
can be the toughest tournament competition, but the subconscious mind will activate him to handle it in just as
relaxed and natural style as the mental images he saw in
hypnosis.

In using self-hypnosis the bowler goes through the
heaviness of limb technique to attain muscle by muscle
relaxation. He takes his pick of hand levitation or eye

closure methods as previously described. He gives himself posthypnotic suggestions, both visual and verbal, for a free and natural style and perfect delivery. Finally, he gives himself the suggestion that he will relax even more deeply the next session and now as he arises he will feel "wide awake, energetic, and wonderful."

It helps the hypnosis process to watch a champion at work. Anybody who has ever attended a championship match or tournament knows that the experience is revitalizing to his or her game. A look at the pros in action never fails to act as valuable "feedback" for the subconscious mind. The next time we play, our subconscious responds loud and clear, so loud and so clear that it survives the usual conscious interference we throw in its way. The result: an inspired serve, a longer drive, a straighter ball.

Dr. David F. Tracy, psychologist to a number of professional teams, and author of *The Psychologist at Bat,* has had considerable success in eliminating nervous tension in players, especially the common type that results when playing before large crowds. He found learning to relax in hypnosis helpful to players for combating before-game tension. Posthypnotic suggestions were then implanted to retain control at all times.

Dr. Tracy's method with young players who become hampered at bat by tenseness and fear would be to tell them while hypnotized that they would be completely relaxed both mentally and physically each time they came up to bat and would have full confidence in themselves and would lean into the ball with every bit of power they could muster.

He reported that the method was also successful with pitchers who tightened up when the chips were down. Here a fixation of attention often developed with the pitcher concentrating on what he should not do instead of on what he should do. If he faced a batter who liked high pitches, instead of visualizing himself pitching a low ball, he saw in his mind's eye the area he wanted to stay away from. This negative approach upsets co-ordination, and, in fact, just as for the golfer who sees the rough instead of the fairway, results in just what is not wanted.

This is hypnotism at work, too. It is the same process that causes poor performance in social and business life.

It is autoconditioning for failure. Each failure increases the fear of another failure. It works just as well as auto-conditioning for success. And it is far more wide-spread.

Negative concentration under pressure can be eliminated for most players through posthypnotic suggestions to the effect that they will visualize exactly what they want to happen; they will see nothing else; they will be confident it will happen. Usually there is an immediate improvement.

The mental side of all sports is crucial. Major attitudes of victory or defeat presage the outcome. Minor attitudes toward missing a shot or making a shot, control the shot. Self-hypnosis and hypnosis can be used much more widely than they are to control this mental side of ice hockey, basketball, tennis, football, bowling, soccer, and other sports. The same type of suggestion—positive visualization—can affect any scoreboard.

As You Think, You Do

Coaches in all sports, from junior high school on up, might do well to know the powers of suggestion. Not that they need to master the techniques of hypnosis. As spell-binders they are practicing a mild form of group hypnosis; but so many of them emphasize the odds against rather than the factors for!

The X team is riding high. They have not lost a game yet. But a big game is approaching and the coach cautions: "We're going to have our hands full. We've got to tighten up on those errors and give it everything we've got!" This builds up fear. It calls attention to errors. A better form of suggestion might be: "Our team is at its prime. We are ready and confident. We know our plays are going great. We are a smooth-working unit, ready to respond to any situation. We have everything we need to win!"

Animals apparently do not have the ability to use their conscious minds to inhibit themselves. They operate fairly consistently at their highest capabilities. The speed at which wild animals are clocked does not change from one decade to the next, while man continues to reach closer and closer to his fullest potential. The four-minute mile was once a dream of track stars. Now it has been broken a number of times. No sooner had Jim Ryun, a University of Kansas freshman established a 3:51.3 record on July 17, 1966, in Berkeley, California, when Kipchoge Keino, a twenty-six-year-old Kenya policeman, turned in a second fastest mile at 3:53.4 on August 20 in London, and set his sights on a try at the record. And so man's time to run the mile will be whittled down to the level that he should have been able to run it right along.

There are some who attribute the shattering of world records to accelerated growth due to better diets and better medical care. They say that aging has slowed, giving athletes more prime years. However, compensating factors are also at work—a more sedentary life in effect. What appears to be really new is the mental horizon. Man is shaking off his shackles of self-limitation.

A competent clinical hypnologist can increase the stamina of a track runner or other athlete faced with tests of endurance. However, the question arises whether or not this poses a danger to the health of the athlete. Will he strain his heart? Or suffer from physical exhaustion? The answer revolves around the nature of the suggestions used. A skilled hypnologist does not give suggestions that encourage a superhuman effort, or any effort beyond the individual's evidenced performance. Rather are suggestions given which eliminate detracting personality or psychological factors. Once these are removed, he can operate at his top efficiency.

"You can" instead of "you will" is not enough. The suggestion must skirt the physical act and devote itself instead to instilling confidence and freedom from tension.

The track star who cannot see himself breaking a record unless he is properly paced, or the wind is at dead calm, or the track just fast enough, sets up conditions which the subconscious proceeds to obey. Through hypnosis, these factors can be neutralized by direct suggestion without physiological harm because they are mental rather than valid physical objections.

Had Mr. Keino talked about his near record run to a hypnologist as he did to the press (he was quoted as saying, "If someone ran ahead of me for the first half then perhaps I could do something" and "I didn't think a world record was possible because I began to feel the effect of a strong wind"), he would be giving the hypnologist the key to exactly what suggestions might be used.

These suggestions could be "You will not feel as though the wind is opposing you, no matter what direction it blows in," and "You can picture yourself now several strides behind a pacer just as you were in a recent race. You will repeat this image in your mind as you try for the record. Whether there is or there is not a runner ahead of you, you will feel the same challenge and the same urge to win."

Hypnotherapy for the Amateur Player

By far the most valuable practical sports application for hypnotism lies not in breaking records but rather in improving the ability of the average beginner or amateur to enjoy the game of his choice and derive the maximum amount of relaxing recreation from it.

Before an amateur can use hypnotism profitably, he must overcome basic faults in his game through watching and imitating or with instruction. A wrong grip or a displaced stance is a self-perpetuating handicap that hypnotism cannot circumvent.

Assuming that the foundation for an average skill exists, here are the suggestions that a hypnologist might give to a beginner bowler who wants to raise his standard of play to the point where he could feel at ease playing with others who have been at it for a number of years:

"I want you to imagine yourself standing at the bowling lanes. You are alone, ready to practice. You are not interested in making any particular score. You have nothing to prove to anyone. You are just there to develop your ability.

"You pick up the ball. It is comfortable to hold. You take your position. You make your approach and your delivery. You follow through. Your movement is graceful and rhythmical. Your manner is relaxed and precise.

"Now I want you to visualize a small friendly boy standing by. He is five or six years old. He is just standing there to enjoy you. You feel quite able and you continue your practicing. Now a second friendly person joins the boy and a third. You feel at ease. You do not feel criticism, only interest.

"Relax more deeply, now. As you remember that all skilled players begin as you are beginning, you feel comfortable. You know that their game has developed just as yours is developing. You feel at ease and comfortable as you bowl with any number of other people. They are a mass of friends without any particular identification. They, too, are in various stages of developing their game. You enjoy your practice. You are confident that you are developing your ability as you bowl with them."

These suggestions, innocuous as they may sound, work wonders in removing inhibiting self-consciousness that plagues so many people. Ego often stands in the way of enjoying even simple parlor games because of the fear that one might look foolish or be inept. You may admire the girl who lets her hair down and joins in, or the fellow who pitches in, in his own inimitable, clumsy way, but you fear to emulate them.

The reason many people do not take up golf despite their attraction to the game is not because it is too far to the course, the price is too high, or they do not have the time or inclination. It is more likely because they have hypnotized themselves with the words "I can't." And behind those words is fear. With the fear there comes a mental image. It could be a fear of missing the ball, of losing it in the trees, of getting into a trap. Regardless of its exact nature, it programs the subconscious to resist. Or if not to resist, then to make a mess of the initial attempts.

The usual negative autosuggestions (on seeing an expert play) run something like this: "My God, I could never play like that. I'll probably be all fingers and thumbs. I'll make a fool of myself."

Counteracting suggestions emphasize interest. You are not expected to be skillful. You are confident that you will improve.

Hypnosis in Manual Skills

An expert court reporter, who operated the stenotype machine with speed and accuracy, found that her job had become a civil service position and that in order to continue in the post, she would have to pass a civil service examination. The examination consisted of taking dictation just as she was accustomed to doing in the courtroom. Even though it was at a slower speed, she failed. She failed the next exam, too, and was in danger of losing her job.

In the first session of hypnotism she was given the suggestion that she had the ability and that she would not look at her fingers. She was asked to visualize herself taking the test and confidently taking dictation looking straight at the person who was dictating. With that she faced the hypnologist and her fingers began to move with lightning speed. She was recording on her imaginary steno-typewriter every word the hypnologist was saying! No further sessions were necessary and the woman now has the required civil service rating.

Manual skills are subconscious skills. Operating office equipment, playing a musical instrument, driving a car. These are all learned through practice and practice means programming the subconscious.

The conscious mind can throw the same monkey wrenches into the works in this kind of learning as in sports. What really slows the learning process is the refusal of the conscious mind to let go and hand it over to the subconscious. When a person gets into a car to do some errands, he visualizes that he must first go to the bank, then the post office, and then the service station. Knowing his route, he gets into the car and drives. He can think about his girl friend or listen to the radio. The subconscious turns right at the light, stops at the stop sign, and pulls up in front of the bank. The conscious mind was able to let go of these menial tasks.

Practice makes perfect. But not if the subconscious is left out in the cold. This happens in self-consciousness. The typist watches her hands. The violinist performs every finger movement deliberately. The person learning how to drive concentrates on his every mechanical action.

The subconscious can be brought into the act by misdirecting the conscious. Perhaps it would be better to say that the subconscious can be permitted to enter the act. For it is there waiting to function, the moment the conscious stands out of the way. The technique of using hypnotism to improve manual skills is simply the removal of conscious interference.

The conscious interference is possible at two stages— the learning and the utilization of learning. At the learning stage the conscious can interfere by lack of attention and concentration. At the utilization of learning, it is quite the opposite; the conscious can interfere by too much attention and concentration.

In learning, conscious attention and concentration provide the visual images that program the subconscious. The utilization of learning calls upon that programming, but the call is futile if the conscious mind insists on "hogging" the line. The subconscious might just as well not have been programmed. It cannot take over.

Hypnotism is used at both stages to improve manual facility. Suggestions that remove fear and negativity and neutralize distraction are custom worded to fit the situation. Suggestions that take the eyes off the fingers and hands and off self are effective in permitting the full utilization of previous practice sessions.

If hypnotism can help a person to enjoy the relaxation of a sport or hobby, its indirect advantages can exceed even the primary goal. These healthful outlets for physical exercise and recreation are also an avenue for discharging certain feelings and emotions. Anger and hostility are inevitable in daily life. They are normal emotions. But they need to be controlled in our society, and therefore they invoke guilt when experienced. Guilt in turn rings the front doorbell of the subconscious and requests punishment. It comes, and in many forms, often as psychosomatic illness.

Anger and hostility are discharged through physical exercise and manual activities. It may not be as obvious as in the case of the salesman who painted his sales manager's face on his home punching bag, or the secretary who used a photo of her boss on her basement dart board. But it is there in football, tennis, and baseball; piano, shop, and knitting. You feel good afterward. Even spectators benefit. "Kill the umpire!"

Hypnotism's advantages in accelerating the acquisition of manual dexterity and sporting skill are being accepted and exploited on an ever widening scale. But this is only a small anteroom in the world of learning. How hypnotism is being used to promote man's intellectual effectiveness hints of unbelievable mental accomplishments possible in the years ahead.

How Hypnotism
Improves Mental Skills

What can we do? What can't we do? Hypnotism is effacing the line between these two areas, as effectively as necessity. Necessity yields what appear to be miracles. A person without arms learns to write with his toes. A mother lifts a car wheel off her child's leg. Man is driven to seemingly superhuman power by need. Actually he has that power the whole time. He just refuses to acknowledge it. In a moment of desperation he forgets his self-image. He can also free himself of it through hypnotism.

A subject under hypnotism believes the hypnologist's suggestions. He performs to the limits of his natural "superhuman" capacity without apprehension. Take memory. Here, for instance, is a typical conversation that might develop between the hypnologist and a middle-aged subject:

Hypnologist: Now I want you to picture yourself as you were at the age of seven. You are in your first grade classroom. The teacher is stand-

	ing in front of you. What is the teacher's name?
Subject:	Mrs. Adams.
Hypnologist:	Tell me the names of the children seated on your right and on your left.
Subject:	Miriam Langley is on my right, Norbert Horst is on my left.
Hypnologist:	Will you describe what each is wearing?
Subject:	Norbert is wearing dark pants and a gray jacket. Miriam has on a brown skirt and sweater.
Hypnologist:	What are you doing?
Subject:	We are taking a test.
Hypnologist:	What is the test about?
Subject:	It is a spelling test.
Hypnologist:	What words are on it?
Subject:	House, ride, play, and, it, good, dog.

The information has always been in the subject's mind. It just had to be reached. Can it be reached consciously? Let's listen again.

Hypnologist:	When I count three you will awaken and you will be able to remember the names of ten other youngsters in your class in first grade. One, two, three. (Subject opens his eyes.) How do you feel?
Subject:	Fine.
Hypnologist:	A moment ago, while you were in a trance state, we were discussing your early years. By any chance, can you remember the names of ten of your first grade classmates?
Subject:	I can remember some quite clearly. Judith Jones, Harriet Fremont, Mary Little, Karen Mittleberg, Joan Spinelli, Grace Miller, Johnny Boyd, Bill Schneider, Frances Keller, and Lynn Smith.

Memory is reachable in hypnosis and also in a conscious state through posthypnotic suggestion. Feats of memory can be made possible by posthypnotic suggestion, first just from time to time, then as a way of life.

Improvement in Memory and Learning

A woman, twenty-two, from England, needed additional college credits in order to be certified as a teacher in New York State. She found the work extremely difficult and seemed to fall apart at examinations. The worse she did, the worse the situation became. It got to a point where she could hardly concentrate on a book open in her hands.

She proved to be a good subject in hypnosis. She could open her eyes during the hypnotic state without disturbing it. This was especially valuable in her case for she was able to follow an interesting procedure. She was asked to open her eyes and read from a book, five or six lines, while hypnotized. She was then asked to close her eyes and was given the suggestion that she could see the book again and the words she had just read. "Now please read them again." This she did quite easily, reading the mental image this time, rather than the book.

The next step was to give this young lady a posthypnotic suggestion to enable her to repeat this procedure at will. "Now whenever you read you will be able to do this again. You will find it quite easy to read, and whenever you wish you can close your eyes and see again exactly what you just read."

To test the effectiveness of this suggestion, she was asked, as she left the office, to pick up a medical journal in the waiting room and read a few lines, then to close her eyes and see if she could read it again. She showed off like a ham actor, rattling off an entire paragraph of medical terminology. The author must admit that even he was flabbergasted. "Now do it backward," he said jokingly. She did, and just as fluently!

In 1955 a report by A. B. Sears was published relating how International Morse Code had been learned at an accelerated rate with the aid of hypnosis. As early as 1934, W. H. Gray reported in the *Journal of Educational Psychology* on the facilitating effects of hypnosis in the ability to spell. Many schools of memory and of speed reading now use modified versions of visualizing techniques that are hypnologically oriented.

Schools and colleges in this country, Italy, and Japan are recording dramatic results in the use of mass hypnotism in class sessions. But the entire field is only dismally explored and sparsely populated.

In the Umejima Primary School of Tokyo's Adachi Ward, Mr. Takehiko Matsukawa, a district school administrator and self-taught hypnotist, is experimenting with a group of fourth grade boys and girls. He uses group hypnosis to improve memory, writing, and reading.

As mentioned earlier, he first leads the group down an imaginary flight of stairs. "With each step down you become more and more relaxed. When you get to the last step you will be completely relaxed. There you are. Now you are very deeply relaxed and in this state you can memorize everything clearly. Let us start the lesson by writing the character 'ko' on your left palm." Eyes closed, the youngsters trace the character on their palms. After going through a whole sentence this way, Mr. Matsukawa claps his hands sharply and the youngsters open their eyes.

There has been much more activity of this type with adults who find their learning ability impaired. Dr. William S. Kroger has helped a number of motion picture, television, and stage performers to learn diffcult roles quickly. His method consists of training the subject in autohypnosis, time distortion, and sensory-imagery conditioning. First, inhibitory factors are reduced and attitudes improved. This is the old story of self-limitation, fear, and anxiety providing stumbling blocks that must be removed. Next, concentration is improved through suggestions that insulate the subject from external stimuli. Then, the lines are memorized. Finally, the subject induces self-hypnosis and visualizes a rehearsal, going through the part again and again. Time distortion is used to condense an hour of action dialogue into five minutes of the subject's time.

This method has also been reported to be highly successful for voice students, musicians, and performers of all types. In many cases, the memorizing of lines is accomplished in one reading by the hypnologist to the subject. This is contingent on a deep stage of hypnosis being attainable, preferably the state of somnambulism. In this state, the person may read and have total visual recall, or be read to and have total aural recall. A by-product of this method has been quality performance. With the conscious mind freed of the necessity for struggling with lines, creativity improved.

Hypnotism and the Mentally Retarded

If the state of hypnosis can be used to improve learning capabilities, is it effective in the training and education of the mentally retarded? Two case histories will be offered from the author's own experience. (If similar work has been done by others, it does not appear to be in medical journals or other published work.)

John, twenty-two, came from a well-to-do family. His mental age was about four. He dressed himself, went to the toilet, and took showers himself. That was it. If he washed his hair, he might soap it but not rinse it. He did not know what day followed Wednesday, or how old he was. He could neither read nor write. He counted to five, sometimes a few numbers further.

Inducing hypnosis in John was quite difficult. He did not respond to visual imagery. "Your arm is getting heavy" meant nothing to him. Eventually success was attained by direct, authoritarian instruction: "You are not to move your arm."

Next, a test was conducted with the multiplication table. It was tried because he evidenced an ability to remember television commercials. He was a continuous viewer and repeated the more common musical couplets on cigarettes and beer. Simple series was repeated such as $1 \times 2 = 2$, $2 \times 2 = 4$, $3 \times 2 = 6$, and $4 \times 2 = 8$. After this was said to him six times, the hypnosis was ended and he was asked to recite the same series. It drew a blank. The process was repeated, this time using three as a multiple so as not to obtain as yet a cumulative result. This time there were twelve repetitions of the series. No results. Nor were there any at twenty or at thirty.

At this point the procedure shifted to tape. The author's voice was recorded and played back to the young man with an automatic repeating device. At the end of the two hundred repetitions, he had total retention. He repeated the multiplication table perfectly, in parrotlike fashion. Albeit no sunrise, some light had dawned.

Now we were ready for some real school work. The first primer was then given the same treatment, page by page. On the first page was a picture of a boy with the name "Bill." He was shown this page and told that when he saw it again he would remember the name "Bill." This simple suggestion was put on the repeating tape and run two hundred times. Out of hypnosis, he was asked to repeat the name of the boy on the page. "Bill." "Good, now say it again and again." A metronome was turned on and with each stroke he recited, "Bill, Bill, Bill . . ."

So it went page after page. It is now three years later. He had gone through first and second grade primers in one and one half hours a week, fifty weeks a year. He can write all of the words in the two books. He can write his name and address. Some of these feats required as much as four hundred repetitions and the patience of Job on the part of the hypnologist. It took a whole year to rid him of an annoying habit of scratching himself which he had had for a dozen years, irritating his skin and causing sores.

There were some improvements in the young man that might be termed indirect benefits. His coordination was better. He responded to such suggestions as "You will be able to do this better." Coming after twenty years of stagnation, it was all very heartening to the parents. However, it would be less than honest not to say that it was anything but heartening to the hypnologist. It was a trying, exasperating experience.

This was alleviated to a degree in the case of a twelve-year-old girl by teaching her parents some of the methods of the hypnologist and transferring to them the ability to place her in a state of mild hypnosis. This girl was infantile in her ways. She could not be toilet trained. She had to be fed. She could not sit still. And to top it off, she was subject to frequent temper tantrums.

The method used was somewhat different, although based on the same principle. While in hypnosis she was put through the motions of social habits. For instance, in the case of brushing the hair, she was told not to move. "You are a doll. You cannot move. Only I can move you. Now I am brushing your hair. I feel you are trying to move your hand. Let me move it for you. Remember, a doll cannot move. That's right. Now I am brushing your hair." To teach her to brush her own hair, the transition had to be gradual: "All right, now you can help me brush your hair." First she helped, then she did it with help. Then she did it herself. For ten to twenty minutes, her hand would be made to brush her hair. Only then was it possible to get results.

She could not be shown how to do anything. She could

only imitate after hours of following the pattern of movement. This applied to dressing and eating and other habits. Her mother supplied the elbow grease that endless repetition required. It paid off. The infant became a small child. She could do all of the things she was laboriously programmed to do.

The tantrums were controlled, also laboriously. They were found to occur at recognizable times, as when her mother put her shoes on for her. Of course, she learned to do this herself, but in the intervening year, temper was controlled by enacting the event under hypnosis in the office and as her temper flared repeating the word "no" as many as a hundred times.

The next step for this child will be another series of "lessons." A clinical psychologist has been asked to provide a set of exercises which will provide her with additional ways to help herself.

Problem Solving

Let us jump about 100 I.Q. points to the above average person who is faced with more difficult than average problems. Hypnotism and what is more often practical to apply here—self-hypnotism—has been eminently effective in enabling the full impact of everything heretofore learned to be brought to bear on a problem in the professions, business, or industry.

An engineer with fifteen years of practice and a record of thousands of exposures to engineering problems was finding that it was taking him an increasing number of tries to hit a right answer. His method was to sit down and try a particular design to see how it solved the structural conditions, then another, and another until possibly the fifth or sixth seemed to do the job to his satisfaction.

Hypnotism helped him in this way: He familiarized himself thoroughly with the problem, all of the conditions that had to be met. Then, in deep relaxation, he would instruct his mind to take over and come up with the solution the next morning. It was like feeding the problem into a computer. The next morning he had the solution on the first try. "I knew that it was the right design as I was putting it down. I even felt I did not have to test it. But, of course I did, and it proved out."

Shades of Bernard Baruch, whose park bench philosophy was to "sleep on it," this is basically a natural function of the brain. It utilizes that vast brain capacity below the conscious level which is so seldom given a chance in this twentieth-century whirl.

The author conducted an experiment based on this method with ten draftsmen. Their problem was to execute a difficult perspective. Five were permitted to proceed as they were without hypnotic techniques. The other five were taught deep relaxation and the suggestive method of activating the subconscious. The experiment was short-lived. The control group was so outdone that they cried "Collusion!" They just could not believe that such an intricate problem could be solved with the facility demonstrated by the five self-hypnotists. Said one of these five later, "All I had to do was follow my pencil."

Another successful method has been passive concentration. This is where the mind is kept blank and the problem's solution permitted to enter. Keeping the mind devoid of thoughts is a difficult if not impossible task for the average person, but through hypnotism and self-hypnotism it is made a relatively simple mental exercise.

An object is needed to capture the thoughts and keep them from wandering. It can be a real object or an imaginary one. A glass of water can act as your "crystal ball" or a spot on the wall. Or you can imagine a blue sky or a gray wall. Imagining a blackboard with the numbers 1 through 10 written there in chalk, and visualizing yourself going up to it ten times and erasing a number at a time until you have proceeded from 10 to a clean slate, is an effective device for centering the mind down to blankness.

Once blank, the request for an answer is made and the subject waits. It may come through immediately or in a few minutes or it might take another session.

A phenomenon known as hyperesthesia is often used in hypnosis to improve learning and skills. The opposite of anesthesia, it can be produced through simple suggestion. It brings on an abnormal capacity of sensory perception. The subject is able to hear better, smell better, see better. The sense of touch can be magnified and sensitized.

Its application in a learning situation is dictated where the environment—either by sound, sight, smell, or some other sensory perception—is impinging on the learner and interfering with his ability to learn or concentrate. If study is being interfered with by sound, say, then hyperesthesia is produced for sight and a mild anesthesia for the unwanted sound. The word unwanted is used advisedly. For it is possible by suggestion to permit wanted sounds, such as those signaling danger or others required by communications, to get through the anesthesia. A certain amount of selection is also possible with hyperesthesia.

A hypnotized person ignores all sounds except what he is told to hear. It is not uncommon to have a sudden noise like the backfiring of a car go unnoticed by the subject as the hypnologist jumps! It is like the mild hypnosis that exists when a person is totally absorbed in what he is reading, and doesn't hear his name called.

A very helpful suggestion for the student is: "Your study is very intense to you. It fills your senses. Outside sounds are unimportant to you. You hear them less and less. Only sounds of danger are recognized by you. Your study is satisfying and attention-filling."

Full Use of the Mind

The practice of hypnotism is so unstructured that nowhere is there even a quasiprofessional society or body where the findings of one sector of a profession using it may be known to the other. Psychiatrists have all they can do to keep up with the latest advances in their own discipline and usually have not the time or inclination to check the psychologists' findings and vice versa. The same might be said of dentists and physicians. As a result, there are splinters of information spread here and there, but not properly coordinated for the good of all.

The use of hypnotism in education, learning, and the increase of mental skills is a case in point. It is being used around the world, but only occasionally does the news filter through to interested parties and even less occasionally does it come through in a form that is usable by others.

The fact is that anything a person can do, he can do better through hypnotism. Abilities are magnified in direct proportion to the knowledge originally stored and the depth of the hypnotic stage. The only limit is an individual's total ability and this is almost always far beyond self-estimate or the estimate of one's peers.

Perhaps full understanding of the brain's magnificent capabilities is known only by the hypnologists, who see at first hand its miraculous workings. Certainly if schools, universities, and industry suspected its potential, there would not be any foot-dragging about using the only technique known to harness its full powers.

There is much talk today about self-understanding. But we seem to know less and less about our attitudes and our anxieties. As Dr. Eric Fromm put it: "Ulcers speak louder than words." Perhaps the reason we turn our back on ourselves is because we are not willing to do anything about what we find out, or else we feel we will not be able to do anything about it.

Hypnotism puts the lie to this; it gives everybody a chance to expand mental and physical horizons. All you have to do is know what you want to improve. The rest is up to the hypnologist or yourself as self-hypnotist.

Hypnotism can do even more than expand known physical and mental abilities. It can develop in many subjects previously unknown abilities that defy scientific explanation and indeed appear to go contrary to accepted physical precepts.

10

Hypnosis and the Paranormal

Frontiers of the mind are in the no-man's-land of science. Just as Mesmer and Braid won the scorn of their professional colleagues, so do parapsychological investigators today brave the brickbats of their counterparts in the more traversed psychic areas.

Hypnotism has brought some marked results when used in the parapsychology laboratory. It has produced measurable increases in clairvoyant abilities of certain subjects. It has similarly affected such paranormal phenomena as telepathy, psychokinesis, precognition, and other types of extrasensory perception. However, it is all as yet unexplainable and inevitably controversial.

Sigmund Freud said, "There are three steps in the history of a great discovery. First, its opponents say that the discoverer is crazy; later that he is sane but that his discovery is of no real importance; and last, that the discovery is important, but everybody has known it right along."

Hopefully hypnotism will be a helpful tool in parapsychology and will speed the day when "everybody has known it right along." But meanwhile, the eminent parapsychological researcher Dr. J. B. Rhine is somewhat less than eminent in some of the hallowed halls of science, and indeed for a scientist who is seeking to further his professional career to even refer to Rhine's work is a profile in courage.

This work will not discuss hypnotism's relation to more distant frontiers. Not for want of courage—the practice of clinical hypnology is proof enough of that—but for want of answers. Researchers differ on the meaning of their results, even on the results themselves. It would not further the understanding of hypnotism to entangle its tender young body in the forces of metaphysical debate. Parapsychology, psychedelia, and other phenomena will have to wait.[1]

There is one exception: time regression. You have seen on the previous pages how hypnosis can distort time. It can shrink minutes of discomfort in childbirth to easy-to-bear seconds. It can bring you back to childhood days with stark reality and total recall. It can do something else.

That something else was called evidence of reincarnation when the book about Bridey Murphy was published. Others call it by other names. It happens often in hypnotism: a person is regressed to childhood or infancy and then appears to remember a life in another time.

Is it play-acting, is it piecing together of previously learned history, is it mediumship, is it evidence of reincarnation? The author does not have the answers. But he has an excellent case history, one that took him by surprise but then, with the cooperation of the equally surprised subject, was observed, recorded, and thoroughly researched.

The rest of this chapter consists of that case history. It is offered with no conclusions, no theories, only abject humility in the light of the wondrous human mind.

The Case of Annie X

The subject, Janet, at the time of this event was twenty-four years old. She immigrated to the United States from England at the age of sixteen. She is an elementary school teacher, married with two small children. The family is reasonably well-off, happy, and well-adjusted to each other

[1] Recommended text: *The Supernatural,* by Douglas Hill and Pat Williams, Hawthorn Books, New York, 1966.

as well as to all elements of society. The subject is attractive, poised and articulate, and displays no signs of emotion instability.

She applied to me for professional services in 1957. She was troubled by an impacted wisdom tooth, which her dentist wished to save, but she did not respond to normal painkillers over the protracted period of treatment. Under hypnotically induced anesthesia the sensitive area remained numb for the required amount of time.

Impressed by these results, Janet applied to me again in the fall of that year, as she was about to take her final exams at college, and wished to enhance her memory potential through hypnosis. It is a matter of record that she subsequently attained "straight A's" in her examinations. More significant, during the course of this hypnotic training a phenomenon occurred, developing out of "normal" age regression techniques.

The Introduction of "Annie"

It is worth noting at this point that there are at least four known states of hypnotically induced memory phenomena: The first is *ABREACTION*, a form of recall in which the subject lives again an episode of his past. The second is *REVIVICATION*, a form of recall in which the subject actually relives a past experience, but is uninfluenced by the accumulation of life knowledge since the original occurrence. The third is *REGRESSION*, which is usually the dramatizing of memories of a past incident. And lastly, *RECALL*, a greater than normal capacity to remember—it may be expressed simply as an oral account in the past or present tense, or as a reenactment of an episode by the subject.

For purposes of probing the subject's subconscious memory potential, recall techniques were applied and Janet immediately proved to be an extraordinary subject. Her capacity for abreaction was almost immediate, and after only a relatively few sessions she was (unbeknownst to her, for like many excellent subjects she has complete amnesia about what occurs during her trance state) experiencing revivication. She was eventually able to reach an actual infantile state—wherein she became, to all intents and purposes, a baby.

Since in this state she was unable to speak of what was

"happening" around her, a technique was developed combining revivication and regression. That is, first Janet would actually relive a given infantile experience (revivication), and then she would be brought "back" to the present, recall the experience, and report upon it.

It is normal procedure for the operator—especially in such sensitive and uncharted areas of application—to periodically ascertain that all is well by "returning" the subject to the present (though maintaining the trance state) and testing her faculties with such simple queries as "What is your name?" and "Where are you?"

I was naturally quite perturbed when, on one occasion, after instructing the subject to "Go as far back as you can, relive that experience, and then be prepared to return and tell me about it," the girl seemed to take an uncommonly long time "returning." I asked her the standard "Do you know where you are?" Long minutes passed and the subject finally shook her head negatively. "What is your name?" I asked.

Again the reply was long in coming. "Annie."

The Life and Times of Annie

Needless to say this session was ended as quickly as feasible and safe. With the subject's permission the next session was attended by several observers. After the next session, the events that were transpiring were related to her and her permission was obtained, with sincere reluctance, to continue a series of similarily observed sessions which eventually numbered forty.

An assistant acted as recorder during most of these sessions and used longhand (the proceedings were rather slow) and tape recordings. Present also at a number of these sessions, which covered the period from March 1956 through February 1962, was a renowned psychiatrist who tested the reactions of the subject in particular trance stages and the authenticity of amnesia about the experience reported by the subject. What follows is a summary of what was recorded.

As a very young child Annie lived in a cottage on cliffs overlooking the sea. The exact locale and time are, as yet, obscured. The only thing "known" is that the setting is Elizabethan England. Annie spent a good deal of her time alone, for her mother died bearing her, and her father was

a sailor, absent from home for prolonged periods of time.
Of her father Annie knows little, except that he was a
kindly man. He told her that before she was born she had
two brothers, both of whom died in infancy. He contributed little to her education or general knowledge, which
may be attributed to the fact that she was very much a
child during this association, and his appearances were
very infrequent. His own education and true station in life
are open to doubt, for while Annie believes he was captain of his vessel, she has no knowledge at all of a family
name.

During her father's long absences, Annie fared for herself mostly, with the sporadic help of some people from
the nearby village. One of these was a woman who tended
to Annie on one or two occasions when she was ill. Another, more regular, visitor was "John," a red-bearded
man who was ostensibly a friend of Annie's father. He
often brought Annie rabbits, which seem to have been her
dietary staple, though she had an aversion to skinning them.
We don't know how Annie occupied her time, other than
that she strolled the beach quite often, and claims to have
occasionally ridden some undomesticated, but seemingly
tame, horses which grazed near her abode.

One day John came to tell Annie that her father would
never return, and it is assumed he was lost in some mari-
time disaster. John wanted Annie to come live with him
in the village, but she found something sinister in his in-
vitation and refused. Soon thereafter she fled in the opposite direction, headed inland, carrying only a few cooked
rabbits for food and taking her only garments—those she
was wearing.

The weather was warm when she left, but she traversed
the forests for some months, apparently, living off the
land. Winter set in, she became too ill to move, and finally
gave up to exhaustion. She was found, near death, by
hunters, and was transported to their home base—some
sort of castle or mansion in the wilderness. There she was
committed to the care of the chief scullery maid, an old
woman named Martha, who nursed her back to health
over a period of months. Upon her recovery she was
given her choice of staying on as a scullery maid or pur-
suing her fortunes elsewhere. Affectionate toward Martha,
the nearest thing to a mother she had ever known, Annie
elected to remain.

Henceforth Martha became the dominant force in Annie's life, but with a fairly large supporting cast. There were "The Master" and "The Mistress," both otherwise nameless, and both of whom, as far as she knows, Annie never once saw. "John," a middle-aged manservant, was apparently the most trusted member of the staff, and all orders to the scullery were relayed through him. There were other servants, some ladies-in-waiting, and household maids; but they were far above Annie's station and she seldom saw or spoke to them. Likewise, the master's "army," a Robin Hoodesque band of huntsmen and warriors, of undetermined number. (They wore a sort of uniform, and it was a detachment of these men who discovered Annie in the woods.) There were two or three stable boys, headed by Steven, who was roguish and held in contempt by both Martha and Annie because he smelled bad and was quarrelsome and licentious.

While we can never be sure of Annie's exact age at any given time, we can make a few assumptions. She was probably between eleven and thirteen years old upon arriving at this domicile (she knows that this was at Christmastime), for the following spring Martha led her to a nearby brook to bathe, and Annie discovered that she was beginning to form breasts.

There's little to be said about her daily life, for it was taken up with preparing meals and cleaning up afterward, apparently working from dawn to dark with scant respite. She did once, early in her tenure at this rich estate, wander into "the house" by mistake, and was awed by the stone steps within, and the rich furnishings. She also witnessed, upon rare occasions, the master's guardsmen jousting, and holding knife and archery drills.

Annie spent her days—and nights—in the scullery. She and Martha slept on pallets before the fire. Her single garment was the one she wore, apparently constructed from some sort of gunny sack, washed infrequently, and replaced whenever it was reduced to tatters.

The high-point—if it can be called that—in Annie's life came three or four winters after she arrived at the estate. She had fallen ill, seemingly with a throat disease which seems to have been a chronic condition. (As Annie, during the hypnotic trance, the subject is often barely audible, complains of a sore throat, and red blotches appear on

her neck.) It was for similar illnesses that the unnamed
woman in her home village sometimes tended Annie.

On one occasion, the head servant, John, was to make
a bartering foray to the nearest large town (which Annie
identifies as "Stratford") and generously invited Martha
and Annie to accompany him. Thinking the change of
scenery would cheer Annie, Martha consented.

The trio traveled, on foot, some three or four days and
nights, mostly through the forest. On the eve of reaching
their destination they had to cross a raging stream, but
in the pitch darkness and a heavy fog, they could not
find the foot bridge which John knew, from experience,
was in the vicinity. Finally John made two swimming trips
across, towing the women. They made camp, cold and
shivering, on the opposite bank, and when they awoke
in the morning the fog had lifted and they saw the missed
bridge only a few yards distant.

Annie's sojourn in "Stratford" was far from the lark
that it might have been. John hastened to conclude his
trading, so they might have one day, out of the time
allotted to him to do business, to spend as they wished.
But upon their arrival Annie fell sicker than ever. The
party was directed to some sort of public house, where
they discovered many people afflicted with the same disease that Annie's proved to be: smallpox.

Countless numbers were dying, and more falling ill
every minute, and the authorities finally ordered the removal of the diseased from the precincts of the town.
John and Martha managed to carry Annie, highly fevered,
to the outskirts, where they discovered an abandoned
shack. They laid Annie to rest there and she remembers
hearing Martha's voice, through her delirium, saying: "If
the blisters break, she'll live." The blisters did break soon
and Annie's condition did improve. In the interim, John
had returned to the estate within the time limit imposed
by the master, and then made his way back to Annie and
Martha's hideaway. En route he stole a horse and Annie
was transported back home on horseback.

She was many months in recovering, and was ever after
very sensitive about her pock-scars, seldom venturing from
the scullery.

She describes herself at this time as being "very small,
with long dark hair, and these terrible marks." (Janet is

small, but not overly petite; fair-haired and with an exceptionally fair and creamy skin.)

At some time during her mid or late teens, Annie was introduced to Roman Catholicism by Martha, that faith being the master's also. It was Annie's first and only religious training, and coming rather late in life, it seems to have been accepted rather than embraced. At that, she was terrified by religion, for Catholicism was outlawed by the crown, and all rites were carried on in secret. Moreover, the master—seemingly a nobleman—was known to be in disfavor with the crown; but whether for religious or political reasons is unknown—as, at this writing, the identity of the "crown."

During this period rites were conducted at a clearing in the forest every sabbath, presided over by someone in resplendent garb, but Annie doesn't know whether this personage was an ordained priest or the master himself, officiating by proxy.

Annie has heard Martha refer to a King Henry as a heretic, and "Lollard" is another of Martha's favorite epithets to describe anyone she suspects of being a religious enemy.

Annie's Demise

Annie's life ended rather abruptly, probably in her late teens or early twenties. Over the years, Steven's advances had become more and more pointed. Finally, he attacked her while she was on an errand to the stable. When Annie refused to submit he knocked her unconscious and raped her. Martha, wondering about Annie's long absence, came in search of her, and drove Steven off, but too late.

In the ensuing months, Annie grew weaker and weaker and Martha told her she was going to have a baby. It is doubtful, at this point, whether Annie ever linked pregnancy to her experience with Steven. Annie eventually began hemorrhaging severely, and, taking to her bed, soon gave birth to a stillborn child. Weak, sick, dispirited, her own death soon followed.

Annie describes her death and subsequent burial. She says her spirit hovered long enough to watch her interment and to witness Martha's grieving, then retired to

limbo. Annie thenceforth resisted "being born again" and
gradually retired from any "conscious" knowledge.

In her age regression as the prime subject—Janet—
the subject's first infantile memory is of a series of very
intense white lights as she was born.

Time and Place of Annie

Though Annie's story is still very inconclusive, and in-
numerable further seances will be necessary to try to pinpoint her place in history, the bits and pieces compiled to
date lead us to infer that she lived probably about the
time of Queen Elizabeth I.

Hitherto unmentioned in this report, Annie has stated
that there seems to have been some seesawing of ascend-
ancy between Catholics and Protestants up to her time.
Henry VIII proclaimed the first wholesale breakaway
from Rome, but his daughter Mary, who succeeded him,
reinstated the faith. On her death, however, her half-sister,
Elizabeth, followed her father's lead and caused the res-
toration of Protestantism in England. Annie's account, then,
seems to indicate that she was around during Elizabeth's
reign.

Also, Annie thinks she has heard of a cargo called
"tobacco," a product introduced to Elizabeth's court by
Sir Walter Raleigh.

Finally, Stratford, England, did not become known as
Stratford-upon-Avon until Shakespeare had passed away.
If the town Annie mentions is the same one, she would
have to have been there during or prior to Elizabeth's
time.

Comparisons Between Janet and Annie

Janet has an unexplained aversion to animal fur. (Annie
despised skinning rabbits.)

Janet has an unexplained aversion to drinking water.
(The smallpox syndrome?)

While Janet is extremely alert and articulate, Annie's
speech is halting and unsure. Her mental processes seem
awfully slow, and she has to add and subtract on her
fingers. The only day of the week she knows by name is
"the sabbath."

Automatic Writing

Numerous attempts to shake Annie's story have been made, to no avail. When reference is made, completely out of hand, to a statement or description of an episode which Annie offered many seances back, her responses and retellings remain steadfast to the original description. Similarly, during one discussion of Annie's having seen the master's guardsmen at drill, Annie was asked to describe their garb, which she did in a not-too-lucid manner. She was then told that later, as much as centuries later, she would, upon a prearranged signal, stop whatever she was doing, take up a pencil, and draw a picture of the guardsmen's headgear. Later, in Janet's normal waking state, the posthypnotic cue was delivered. Without knowing why she was doing it, she took up a pencil and drew a picture of a bearded man wearing a sort of beret with a tassel dangling to one side. She could not explain why she had felt compelled to draw this picture. Her drawing was removed and she was asked to try to duplicate the picture she had just drawn. This conscious act took a great deal more deliberation and time on her part, she had to think a great deal about the details of the hat she was copying from memory, and the overall quality of the drawing was cruder that the first effort.

Other Techniques Employed

As a subject, Janet has been so highly trained that the trance can be induced instantly on a prearranged posthypnotic signal. Likewise, by use of a prearranged code, she can be "switched" from Janet to Annie, during the hypnotic state, with great rapidity.

Three methods of interrogation of Annie have been employed. The first was to merely ask questions as an omnipresent voice. Replies from Annie were exceptionally slow and monosyllabic. Then a third person was introduced as a contemporary of Annie, but this method reduced the subject to complete confusion, as the "contemporary's" acts and speeches were completely out of Annie's context. The third method has proved most successful in drawing her out. The omnipresent operator directs that Annie relive an experience and then, questioned, report on it a length and in detail. The following is a tape transcript of a typical session. It was preceded by the introduction into the session of the "automatic writing" technique. In the trance state (as Annie) the subject was given a pen and permitted to scribble at will. She was then returned to her true identity (Janet) and told to explain the scrawlings. She was unable to do so, whereupon Annie was brought back, and the following conversation ensued.

Annie: (Sigh.)

Hypnologist: Tell me about the marks you made.

Annie: This is my sign here. We all had to have signs. Martha taught me how to do this, counting the chickens. I had to check with these . . . with these marks. Then if I checked the chickens that day, this was my sign to go (buy or by) them. Sometimes the master would want things checked to see how much stuff he had . . . and this was Martha's sign, she chose herself.

Hypnologist: And this sign over here?

Annie: This is Martha's sign . . . these are all Martha's signs.

Hypnologist: Do you think you could do Martha's sign again . . . over there? . . . And the little dots here—what do they form?

Annie: (Hesitantly, sighing, hint of counting under breath.) This is when there was more than we could count, we just made a dot for every one that passed us . . .

Hypnologist: And this shape over here?

Annie: (Long pause.) This is my sign again . . . but it's not very (unintelligible. Sounds like wahr or well or wide).

Hypnologist: Uh huh . . . and that sign here.

Annie: (Pause, sigh, hesitantly.) That's Martha's sign again but I think (drops to whisper) I had tried to take it away when . . .

Hypnologist: (Interrupting a seeming train of thought.) Did everybody have a sign?

Annie: Yeah . . .

Hypnologist: Did Steven have a sign?

Annie: Yes.

Hypnologist:	Did you ever see it?
Annie:	(Weakly, with hint of trepidation.) Yes.
Hypnologist:	Show me what it looked like.
Annie:	It was just this . . . (drops to whisper) . . . just a heavy . . .
Hypnologist:	(Drowning out her last words.) The same as Martha's sign . . .
Annie:	No, it was just a heavy—
Hypnologist:	Uh huh.
Annie:	—thick line.
Hypnologist:	Who else had a sign? Did John have a sign?
Annie:	Yes, we all had signs. But John could— John had more than one. (Pause. Heavy breathing.)
Hypnologist:	What sign did John have?
Annie:	Should I make it?
Hypnologist:	Uh huh.
Annie:	(Under breath, barely audible) . . . know whether I can . . . was like . . . (long pause, then louder) it was like this . . . seree (inaudible: was three was very?) . . . 'cause he was . . . he was more important 'n we were. (Deep sigh.)
Hypnologist:	What did you make the sign with?
Annie:	When we were counting we used to do it in the . . . outside in the dirt with a stick. We counted like this . . .
Hypnologist:	Uh huh.
Annie:	(Heavy respiration.)
Hypnologist:	Do you remember the time when you and John and Martha went to the village? (Reference to Stratford, during which Annie contracted smallpox.)
Annie:	Yes.
Hypnologist:	Do you remember the beginning of that? How did that trip come about?
Annie:	(Very low.) Well, we (pause, then louder) —we were working very hard . . . been a a long winter I think . . . I never saw the master, but he told John to take . . . take us all . . . to take two of us . . . of anyone he pleased . . . to go down to town (voice picks up trace of dialect in words

down t'town) and get ta (as in Yorkshire
dialect for "the") provisions . . . so he was
very nice, he chose Martha and I go with
him. We were very excited. (Long pause,
heavy breathing, sense of effort in speaking.) I wish I hadn't got sick for him . . .
caused him a lot of trouble. (Long pause.)
That's how we got to go on ta trip—through
John. (Long pause during which Annie
sketches a head—)

Hypnologist: Who is that?

Annie: (Pause) . . . looks a bit like John. . . .
A sad face . . . had a crooked nose . . .

Hypnologist: Did he have long hair like that?

Annie: (Dreamily.) Uh huh.

Hypnologist: Did you ever do that (draw) before?

Annie: I don't think so . . . It's very hard with
(inaudible; sounds like "na ta wing." Not
knowing?) . . .

Hypnologist: Did you ever try to do it?

Annie: We often used to go outside . . . while
we had time . . . we used to try making
face 'n shapes . . . patterns . . .

Hypnologist: Uh huh. Were you good at it?

Annie: No . . . I . . .

Hypnologist: Was Martha good?

Annie: (Emphatically.) No! John was . . . (heavy
sigh) . . . John was the best . . . (Heavy
sigh.)

Hypnologist: What kind of pattern did he used to make?

Annie: He used to draw—he loved the hills. He
used to say he was going to have a little
house . . . all by himself . . . with a little
door (Annie begins drawing) . . . there'd
be lots of trees . . . and nobody would
bother him here. . . . 'd be a little stream
through here . . . I'd like to have gone
there with John.

Hypnologist: Did John move away?

Annie: No. (Long pause.) This is where John
wanted to live.

Hypnologist: Uh huh. You talk about everything as if
it had already happened. You said that's
where John wanted to live . . . and that's

	what John used to do. Is it a long time ago you're thinking of?
Annie:	(Dreamily.) Uh huh. (Long pause.) . . . Had (or have) lotta time to think. (Long pause, heavy breathing.)
Hypnologist:	What are you going to do tomorrow?
Annie:	(Long pause.) I don't think there's going to be a tomorrow for me. (Long pause.) I feel . . . so easy now. Pains all gone. No time to think. I think I'm looking forward to going.
Hypnologist:	(Long pause.) Are you going to miss anyone?
Annie:	I'll miss Martha . . . and John . . . because I think they'll miss me.
Hypnologist:	What do you think is going to happen to you tomorrow?
Annie:	I don't think my body's got any more strength left . . . and I'll have to go.
Hypnologist:	Would you like to come back into the world again?
Annie:	I think I will.
Hypnologist:	How would you like to live?
Annie:	(Indicating picture of John's dream house.) I'd like to live like this.
Hypnologist:	Up on the hill . . .
Annie:	(Dreamily.) Uh huh. Like I've seen lots of people do. (Or "Like to see lots of people too.")
Hypnologist:	Do you think you're coming back?
Annie:	Martha seemed to think everyone did. She said they lived on and on . . . if they were good people. I think I've been a good person. (Long pause.) . . . not yet. I want to rest for a little while. (Draws something.)
Hypnologist:	What is that?
Annie:	(Long pause, resignedly.) That's probably where they'll put me to rest. One of the maids died in the . . . plague . . . a few months ago, and this (voice breaks slightly) is what they did with her.

11

Misconceptions, Dangers, Limitations

Ask people what they think it might be like to be hypnotized and you get answers such as "It's like being asleep" or "You're paralyzed" or "You lose control of yourself to someone else."

What is it really like to be in a state of hypnotism? It is neither sleep, paralysis, nor loss of control. But it may borrow some characteristics of all three. Ask people who have been deeply hypnotized and you get answers such as "You feel like you are in an inner room of yourself—the quiet place" or "You feel like you are floating in space" or "You feel like you are at the door listening in."

Perhaps, in order to get an easy-to-grasp description of the hypnotic state, we should ask somebody who has listened to a television commercial or read a newspaper ad, for they too have been in a suggestive state. How did you feel, we inquire, when the announcer came on holding up that bottle of new "X" detergent? "Oh, I was nice and relaxed and did not feel like turning him off." "Were you listening to what he was saying?" "I can't say I gave him my undivided attention, but I guess I heard what he said." "Did what he said make you want to get up and buy 'X' detergent?" "No, I wasn't particularly interested in any detergents then." "Well, thank you for your help." "You're quite welcome." "Oh, one last question: What detergent do you use?" "I use that 'X' brand now."

Misconceptions about just what the state of hypnosis is really like are not only common among laymen but also in professional circles. It would be difficult to get two physicians to describe the state of hypnotism in exactly the same way. They vary all the way from "It's like sleep" to "It's all in the imagination."

Even dictionaries do not exactly agree. Webster's Unified calls hypnosis a "trancelike sleep." Funk & Wagnalls calls it a "trancelike condition resembling sleep" and the *Dictionary of Psychology* [1] a "state usually (though not always) resembling sleep, but physiologically distinct from it."

Hypnosis Is Not a Sleep State

The hypnotized subject is in a state of complete lethargy. He moves listlessly in response to suggestions. His arms droop limply at his sides. His head falls on his chest. There is a lack of expression in his features. Certainly all of this comes close to describing sleeplike characteristics. But hypnosis is not sleep.

There may be no word in the English language to describe what it is more accurately than does the word sleep. But sleep is not even distantly related to hypnosis and there needs to be a word other than sleep to describe the state of hypnosis.

There also needs to be a word meaning to end the state of hypnosis as "awake" means to end the state of sleep. Hypnotists use the words "wake up" for want of better ones, and in the process they perpetuate the misconception that there is a relationship between hypnosis and sleep. Perhaps "arouse" comes closer than "awake."

The fact is that a person may be hypnotized and be just as wide awake as when he walked into the room a few minutes before. He may be able to open his eyes and still be hypnotized. He may also fall asleep while in a state

[1] H. C. Warren, ed., *Dictionary of Psychology*, Houghton Mifflin Co., Boston, 1934.

of hypnosis, especially if a suggestion to do so is given, and he will then be in an entirely different state, one in which the power of suggestion is not magnified as it is in the state of hypnosis.

A person who is hypnotized is aware of what the hypnologist is saying and aware of his own thoughts. This auditory and intellectual awareness is not total consciousness and critical awareness but it *is* awareness. In fact, it is a state of increased awareness to the extent that the subject is paying full attention to the operator's instructions. This concentration involves more of the total mind than is normally involved in conscious attention.

The equating of hypnosis with sleep is a misconception that is often taken right into the state of hypnosis by the subject. As a result, the first thing he often says on the termination of the session is, "I was not really hypnotized. I heard everything you said."

This misconception can inhibit both the induction and management of the state of hypnosis. Disbelief counteracts that state. Belief enhances it. Reluctance to fall asleep creates a resistance to being hypnotized even though they are not one and the same.

Removing the misconception makes for a better subject. A good way to do this is to explain that hypnosis, contrary to the way it is portrayed in movies or on the stage, is not a state of sleep, but is rather the dreamy, attentive state of a music lover listening enraptured to subtle variations of a symphonic theme. The state is one of alertness and concentration, even though the eyes are closed and the body completely relaxed.

While the subject feels little, if any, change in his mind, the observer sees a number of changes that confirm the existence of hypnotic stages one through fifteen, or even higher. He sees the tension disappear from the body and the face. He sees the general appearance of drowsiness and then the fluttering of the eyelids just prior to closing.

The observer notes that the lifting of the arm, in the levitation method, is unnatural. Breathing is slower and deeper. If the pulse were taken, it would be found to be slower. Then, when asked to "awaken," there is an involuntary start.

There may be no loss of consciousness in hypnosis until beyond the thirtieth stage, and since few subjects can reach this stage, it is a rather rare condition and one which does not belong in the popular conception of a typical state.

"You Can Make Me Do Things Against My Will"

Several years ago, a group of hypnologists in an experimental clinic conducted a number of tests to see if a person who was very deeply hypnotized could be made to do things that were against his better judgment.

Thirty persons were subjected to the suggestion that they were to sign a legal paper assigning over to another person their property and money. A plausible explanation was given for the suggestion by the hypnologists conducting the test. All thirty were in a deep, somnambulist state where no memory of the suggestion is carried over. Not one was persuaded to sign the paper. Instead, one reaction was "I cannot move my hand," and others scribbled meaningless scrawls or professed not to understand. Some became quite agitated and the session was terminated.

Another set of nine somnambulists participated in another test. They were told that they had inherited a considerable amount of money. They were then given the suggestion that they would celebrate this event on New Year's Eve and invite all six hypnologists in the clinic. The total expense, it was suggested, might be about $250. This was a posthypnotic suggestion which contained an element of urgency. It failed to evoke a single invite. In twenty minutes, each subject was rehypnotized so as to remove the fictitious story of inheritance lest it cause trouble later. One subject did call a few days later to see if one of the hypnologists might join him for a New Year's Eve party. But he never did call back to confirm the invitation.

Attempts were made by the same experimental group to test the results of suggestions to the effect that there would be a change of religion. Some forty subjects took part in this, yet not one was affected by the suggestions that they were dissatisfied with their present religion and interested in another.

Dr. Platov of Leningrad University reported in a paper prepared for the University that in fifty years of practice with fifty thousand subjects he had never found a subject that would do something either in hypnosis or by posthypnotic suggestion that he or she would not do under normal motivation.

Taking a look at the other side of the coin, what about those stories that occasionally crop up in the press where a crime has been committed allegedly through the effects of hypnotic control over one person exercised by another? There is no doubt that persons in hypnosis have been encouraged to do things they might not otherwise feel it right to do. The same is true of people under the influence of narcotics or liquor or even just bad company. One well-documented case of murder ostensibly via hypnotism involved the subject's development of close emotional attachment to the emotionally unbalanced hypnotist over a long period of time. The same sequence of events would very likely have occurred without hypnotism. Another published case involved a prisoner of war committing criminal acts through posthypnotic suggestion. Here again it seems likely that the same acts would have been performed by strong persuasion.

Many are the stories about certain behavior at office parties—an otherwise sedate girl may be swept free of inhibitions by the sheer revelry. Although the author cannot recite any case histories, this kind of thing could happen in hypnosis, as well.

The innate desire for sexual relations, suppressed by social mores and religious teaching, moves closer to expression when the onus of conscience is temporarily set aside. This setting aside is a conscious act. The subject says in effect, "I am now blameless because I am under the influence of liquor (drugs) (hypnotism)."

If a hypnologist were to make an improper suggestion to a subject, she might grasp the opportunity to separate herself from reality, knowing that she could later claim that she did not know what she was doing. It is therefore theoretically possible for a hypnotist to raise the emotional level in a subject and induce sexual desire. It is just as possible for a physician or psychiatrist or psychologist to do this, for a similar rapport exists in these relationships. A hypnologist would no sooner take such a chance with his professional career than would these other professional people.

One often hears that the patient "falls in love" with the therapist. Doctors and psychotherapists are no more immune than hypnotherapists. There is an erotic basis in any relationship where rapport and transference are present. But this does not mean that a person must act out his or her sexual fantasies in the doctor's office or in a hypnotic session. In fact, there is no real danger that he or she will.

The person who is at heart a thief can be lifted by hypnotic suggestion over the hump of conscience that has kept him straight. He can also be lifted over that hump by due need, or extreme temptation, or the repeated exhortations of his lighter-fingered cronies.

Acts of violence are possible and impossible for the same reasons. They cannot be motivated in hypnosis unless they can be motivated normally.

Occasionally an action in a hypnotic test appears to contradict this. For instance, a penny is dropped into sulfuric acid and the subject is shown the disintegrating effect of the acid. The suggestion is then given: "There is a man about to enter who is bent on murder. Your only defense is to throw the acid in his face." The acid is unobtrusively replaced with a similar container of water. An associate opens the door and enters. The subject flings the liquid at him!

When this occurs and the subject is advised of the implications there is usually an explanation to the effect that "I trusted you. You would never have allowed an injustice to happen. I just knew it was all right." The fact is, the liquid *was* harmless. And if instead the acid was retained and a wax dummy used instead of a man, the act would still be harmless. Remove these props and replace them with a true plot to assault and there is a plethora of evidence that the subject would be an unreliable accomplice.

The misconception that you can be controlled by the hypnotist against your will will no doubt linger on. But meanwhile those who are sincerely interested in the therapeutic benefits that hypnosis can afford should acquaint themselves with the true facts:

1. A skilled clinical hypnologist is an ethical person who knows there is no guarantee that the suggestion for amnesia will work and will be sustained indefinitely. He has, therefore, the same motivation for the maintenance of ethical conduct as has any other professional person.

2. A subject lives and behaves within the same moral code under hypnosis as normally.

"I Am Afraid to Hand My Mind Over to Someone Else"

Many persons who can benefit from hypnotherapy have mental reservations about its involving a surrender of will. This misconception either stops them from seeking hypnotherapeutic help or interferes with their adequacy as a subject.

The idea that the hypnotized subject hands his mind over to the hypnologist is just as erroneous as the popular misconceptions concerning hypnotism's potential in sex and crime. The myth is based on the Svengali image that is perpetuated in motion pictures and on television. Hypnotists are depicted as all-powerful and dominant. They are usually cast as beetle-browed males with strong, overbearing personalities and few scruples.

The truth is that the best hypnologists are sensitive and permissive in nature. They do not have to have strong, dominant personalities. Women make every bit as good hypnologists as do men. And a male hypnotist can be a good subject for a female hypnotist.

One does not have to hand one's own mind over to someone else in order to have it changed for him. What is feared as the exclusive and insidious power of hypnotism is an everyday matter through the continuous flow of information in mass communications. We are all constantly being bombarded with suggestion in all degrees of subtlety and persuasion. Speeches, news stories, propaganda, and advertising exercise control over millions of minds every day. Mass psychology is a form of mass hypnotism.

Nothing about all of this changes during the hypnotic session. You change your attitude and behavior only if you are convinced you want to. The obese person changes from carbohydrates to proteins because an agreement to do so has been reached before the hypnosis session. Suggestions given to this effect are welcomed and will support that agreement quite effectively. Suggestions given to the effect that the subject will also stop smoking will fail dismally. Similarly, the person who volunteers for hypnotherapy to stop smoking will find such suggestions in hypnosis dramatically successful, while off target suggestions to change eating habits, not previously agreed to, will be shrugged off.

Brainwashing as used on prisoners of war is a case in point. If hypnotism could be used to inspire ideas and beliefs on an unwilling subject, there would be no need for long months of torture inflicted on prisoners—days without sleep, weeks in solitary confinement, food and other rewards only after yielding step by step in the agonizing process.

It bears repeating that in hypnosis there is no loss of consciousness. The subject is in control. There is no loss of awareness. There is no loss of will, except to the extent that you are following simple instructions. These instructions are often just as innocuous as "No smoking" signs, or "Watch your step."

How about a hypnologist attempting to hold a patient or increase the frequency of visits by a suggestion such as "You will want to repeat this relaxing session here again very soon and often"? It might work. There is no doubt that similar suggestions to return soon for another examination work for a physician. And often they do not work. The original determining factors, be they time, inclination, or money, are more likely to remain the determining factors.

On the other hand, if a subject requested help from a hypnologist to adhere to a strict schedule of appointments, then a full force suggestion would be unleashed. Conviction, expectations, and belief, all coupled with the reality of the "as if" principle, would produce the exact effects *invited* by the subject.

Another aspect of mind control envisioned erroneously by many would-be subjects is secret divulgement. They are afraid that the state of hypnosis is like truth serum and, on command, the hypnotist can extract innermost secrets. Here again there is an element of truth involved but it is still basically a misconception..

If you ask a person in the conscious state where he was Wednesday night and he lies to you, you will get a lie also in the hypnotic state. Only a skilled hypnologist, using intricate techniques, and able to induce a very deep stage of hypnosis, has any chance of getting at the truth against a person's conscious will.

One method is the technique of automatic writing described earlier. Here the subject is given the illusion that his hand is separated from him and no longer under his control. The subconscious does the rest.

Another method that can be used by a skilled hypnologist is to create the illusion that he, the hypnologist, is another person, one who is known to the subject and to whom the information sought is not secret. The subject will then divulge the secret because he is not aware that he is breaking a trust. He fully believes he is discussing it with the "in" person.

"Only the Weak-Minded Can Be Hypnotized"

The history of hypnosis is replete with condemnation and misrepresentation. Ever since the days of Mesmer, exploitation, distortion, and abuse have dogged its progress. As recently as twenty-five years ago, scientific journals published papers by persons of otherwise excellent reputations who labeled hypnosis as fraudulent, indicating collusion between the subject and the hypnotist.

Some of the more generous critics and self-styled debunkers labeled hypnosis as a state that could be inflicted only on the gullible or weak-minded. That mistruth has survived as a misconception which is still quite prevalent today.

Here the truth is not a matter of yes and no. The good subject is unequivocally the intelligent subject. Suggestibility is not gullibility. Suggestibility is a sensitivity to one's own imagination. It profits not the hypnologist who is seeking to implant a suggestion to entertain an image in in his own mind. That image must be visualized by the subject in *his* mind. To visualize requires a good imagination and good mental control.

Concentration and intelligence are absolutely essential to hypnotic induction. The ability to think abstractly comes more quickly to the more intelligent. It is almost totally absent in the imbecile and he usually cannot be hypnotized.

Doctors, dentists, and psychologists who take a course in hypnotism at college and, as a part of that course, practice on their colleagues, get excellent results due to the high intelligence level prevalent in those professions, and are sometimes floored later by the increased difficulty in attaining similar states of hypnosis in the more average patients.

A person often says, "I can't be hypnotized," to point up the strength of his intelligence when in actuality the opposite is indicated. The only valid reasons that prevent an intelligent person from being hypnotized are these very misconceptions and fears.

If an intelligent person has learned somewhere that a stage hypnotist inadvertently left one of his subjects in a state of hypnotism, the fear has been implanted. "Suppose I can't wake up?" Unless the hypnologist learns of this fear in the initial interview, the attempt at hypnosis will very likely be a fiasco. Once this fear is expressed to the hypnologist, he can then explain that there is no known way to keep a person in a state of hypnosis. (The longest known case was one involving an insomniac kept in a state of hypnosis for four days by a team of hypnologists.) If a person is left in a state of hypnosis, he will get bored and wake up. Or he might fall asleep and wake later. In either case, he will be his normal self on awakening.

People have a general fear of the unknown. To many, hypnotism still conjures up the mysterious and mystical. Even the scientist, professional man, or educator will decline to be a subject, fearing some kind of damage to his mind, or loss of power. Understanding hypnotism is an important step to the full exploitation by mankind of its therapeutic benefits. That understanding will remove invalid beliefs and permit valid use. That understanding will retain valid reservations and prohibit misuse. For hypnotism can indeed be misused. In the hands of the untrained and ill-intended the unexpected can happen.

"I Can Be a Hypnotist in a Few Hours of Practice"

The scene is a resort hotel. It is the height of the season and the capacity crowd is looking forward to the evening's entertainment, billed as "Sam Brown—Hypnotist Extraordinary." What they do not know is that Sam is about go on stage for the first time. What he knows about hypnotism he has just learned from a dollar handbook.

Even before he comes on stage, Sam knows that extroverted persons are quite likely to be sitting down front and the more introverted persons have gravitated naturally to the rear. Therefore, his most willing volunteers are close to the stage where he can observe them carefully.

The laudatory introduction is made. Sam comes out on the stage. The audience believes they are about to witness a performance by a seasoned hypnotist. That's very important; Sam has the battle half won already. Sam starts his performance with a brief talk about the benefits of hypnotism. He speaks well and knows his facts. He gains the confidence of the audience. Another important step toward hypnotism has been successfully accomplished.

Next, Sam says that he is now going to perform an interesting experiment. He asks the entire audience, numbering about three hundred, to participate. "Clasp your left and right hand together," he instructs. "Now look at your hands intently. I am going to count to three. When I reach three you will be unable to separate your hands. Ready? One! Your hands are fixed tighter and tighter together. Two! They are as tight as a vise. Three! (In a commanding voice.) *No matter how hard you try, you cannot separate your hands.*"

Let us go on the stage at this moment and look at the audience the way Sam sees it. Several people in front are struggling with their hands and cannot separate them. Others are able to separate them after an initial struggle. They get quite a kick out of it and talk excitedly with others in the group. However, most of the audience have little trouble in unclasping their hands immediately. Little matter; Sam is doing fine.

Sam then asks those whose hands are still clasped to come up on the stage and be seated. He knows he has four or five, maybe more, excellent pretested subjects. He walks up to each one in turn. He tells the subject that he may unclasp his hands, but that when Sam shakes hands with him he will fall fast asleep. As he shakes hands with each subject, Sam watches the reactions carefully. The first, a businessman, closes his eyes. The second, a young girl about seventeen, closes her eyes and her head slumps to her chest. Here is his first victim. After he has gone down the line with varying results, he comes back to the girl.

Sam has now followed the book more than half the way through. He has several excellent subjects on stage, selected from three hundred people. These subjects are the somnambulists, rare even in a hypnologist's practice.

Now he is free to go wherever his imagination will take him.

"Now, Miss, I am going to give you this pair of glasses. They are very unusual glasses. With them you can see through everybody's clothing. When I clap hands I want you to awake and put on the glasses." He claps his hands. The girl opens her eyes. Sam hands her the glasses and she puts them on. Her jaw drops and she begins to shriek. She turns a crimson red and turns her back to the audience. Once again she turns slowly around, to confirm what she has seen. Again she shrieks and puts her hands over her eyes.

Sam has the audience in the palm of his hand. They sit enraptured as he creates illusion after illusion for his subjects. He brings the orchestra into his act by asking them to play "Melancholy Baby." He gives the suggestion that when his stage subjects hear the first few notes of that song they will fall back into their deep sleep. Several times during the act, the orchestra strikes up that melody and no matter what they are doing the subjects relapse into their trance.

When it is all over, Sam gets a big hand. He knows that this success will make it easier for him the next night as his reputation paves the way for greater confidence and expectation in his audience.

What he does not know is that the following morning one of his subjects contributes to the holiday traffic fatalities. The police report states that the victim apparently lost control of the car. They make no note of the fact that the car radio was on at the time of the crash. Certainly they have no way of knowing that the tune on the air at the moment was "Melancholy Baby."

Sam's career is just beginning. The very next night he has six persons on the stage. The audience has been convulsed by their antics. First, he describes an Arctic scene. "You are freezing in bitter cold weather without an overcoat." They blow in their hands, slap their bodies, jump up and down. "It is July on the Equator. It is stifling." They wipe their brows, fan themselves.

"You are now in a plane. You are parachutists. When I count ten, you will jump. You will then float gracefully to earth." Sam does not notice that at the count of seven, one of the male subjects turns ashen. Still watching his audience rather than his subjects, Sam reaches nine and the man keels over. Sam never gets to ten. Gasps come from the audience. Several men run up on the stage and bend over the prostrate subject. Someone yells, "Get a doctor." Sam is pretty pale himself. He wakes each of his subjects hurriedly and asks them to return to their seats. The man is carried off the stage to the wings. A few minutes later a doctor arrives. He can tell at a glance that it is a heart attack. The man is taken in an ambulance to a nearby hospital. Before it pulls away, Sam is notified by the manager that the rest of his booking at that hotel is canceled.

There are other hotels. A stage hypnotist is always in demand. The scene now shifts to another resort, another stage, another week. A woman of fifty-five is told that she is getting younger and younger. She is now fifteen. It is springtime, she is walking in the park. Suddenly the woman is terrified. She begins to scream. Sam tries to awaken her. It is to no avail. She lashes at him and appears to be striking out at an unseen adversary. Sam asks for help from two men seated in the audience, as he awakens and dismisses his other subject. Another show has ended unexpectedly. The next day Sam finds out why. A psychiatrist called in to treat the now hospitalized and still hysterical woman explains that the woman was raped in a park as a young girl of fifteen and is now reliving the agony of the experience. Sam is reassured that he had no way of knowing this, that she will be all right in a week or so, and that it was not really his fault.

Or was it.

Managing the state of hypnosis is like walking through a mine field. It is not for the novice. Being a stage hypnotist requires careful training, as most veteran stage hypnotists will confirm, just as careful as that received by the clinical hypnologist. For the same human minds are at work, the same lives at stake.

Is Hypnotism a "Cure-All"?

Watching a stage performance by a hypnotist gives the average person very little if any increased understanding of the phenomenon. In fact, he probably comes away with a sense of having witnessed something bizarre and mysterious, and all the more removed from the sphere of down-to-earth, practical utility.

At the other end of the spectrum of misunderstanding is the person who is so awed by the phenomenon that he is ready to believe anything about it—especially that it can cure any incurable disease. Those who claim for hypnosis the impossible do the science perhaps an even greater injustice than the scoffers.

Hypnotism is far from being a cure-all. For some subjects it is a cure-nothing. For others it is a little better. The best that can be claimed for hypnotism is that in most subjects some improvement is possible in most conditions. Though this may have the ring of a watered down statement, on further analysis it is perhaps the broadest claim that can be made for any known drug or therapy.

Certainly, as a field of scientific inquiry and method of psychotherapy, hypnotism, compared to other approaches, deserves many more times as much attention as it is getting from those concerned with the science of human health and behavior. Hypnotism's failings do not derive, at present, from the method itself but from those who apply it. Greater experimentation, better training, more knowledge can lead quickly to broader areas of success both with more difficult subjects and with their conditions.

It is the physician's responsibility to recognize the potential for cure and recommend a particular approach to the patient. This recommendation, however, is seldom that the patient try hypnotism, even where hypnotism offers some hope. In fact, it is usually the patient who recognizes this hope and suggests hypnotism to the physician. One would think that the quality of mercy would in itself prompt the physician to encourage the patient to seek hypnotherapy. But the many wheels of progress move at different paces and for some the movement can be temporarily impeded by pride and prejudice.

Even for a hypnologist in daily practice, hypnotism offers some surprising results. A woman, whom the author treated successfully for alcoholism, asked if she might bring her daughter to the office. The girl was a victim of polio and was completely paralyzed in both legs. She had been under the care of an excellent physician and physiotherapist. There was no progress. The diagnosis of her condition had been competently prepared. The prognosis was negative.

Since both the mother and daughter were quite insistent,

the author spoke to both the physician and the psychotherapist. They agreed that there was "no hope" and inferred that anyone who would think there could be rejuvenation of destroyed nerve tissue was something of a charlatan.

That settled it. I would see the child. In fact, I would go to her home. I had little hope in this particular case, but infinite hope for hypnotism.

She was a willing and deep stage subject. First, the suggestion was made that her right arm (both arms were in good condition) had a cord tied to the wrist. The other end of the cord went up to the ceiling where it passed through a hook and hung down within reach. "When I pull on the string, your arm will lift. You will not be able to hold it down. The tension will be too great. Even if you tried to and struggled it must rise. I am pulling." The hypnotic suggestion did its work. The arm rose. She was asked to look at her arm and see it raised.

Now for a paralyzed leg. The same image was painted, this time with the cord tied around her right leg. "As I pull on the cord, your leg will move up. I am now pulling."

For a moment there was nothing. Then there was a quiver. A slight movement. "Look at your leg, it has started to move." She looked, saw the very slight movement, and started to cry.

Her mother persuaded the psychotherapist to attend the next session. The experiment was repeated with similar, possibly even slightly better results. He was amazed at the movements. He agreed to join with me in a series of treatments. In six months the girl was standing with the help of crutches and using some leg muscles. It was not a cure. But it was a blessing.

In many cases of paralysis, there is no organic basis for it but still no known medical cure—except hypnotism. Such paralysis is a form of hysteria and once the subconscious cause can be brought to the surface, an immediate and dramatic cure can result.

Such a cure may never be possible where an organic cause, such as polio, produces the paralysis. But the case of this young girl, and many other cases like it, indicate that increased experimentation is needed to enlarge the knowledge and improve the skill of the hypnologist. There is no doubt that this could lead to further progress toward cure in many "incurable" conditions.

There is nothing miraculous about hypnotism. The

trance state is no "open sesame" to the impossible. The same limitations that prevent a subject's responding to immoral or harmful suggestions can often apply to suggestions that are therapeutically helpful. Deeply rooted neurotic symptoms often defy removal by suggestion. If a patient is not properly motivated he will not respond. This is perhaps the most common reason behind the failure of hypnotism to change attitudes, remove symptoms, or encourage more positive attitudes toward people and life.

Failure comes too when a subject cannot be induced into a deep enough stage of hypnosis for effective use of suggestion. Here teamwork between psychiatry and hypnology can make headway. It is often easier for the psychiatrist to determine what reasons militate against the subject's willingness to be hypnotized. Once these are recognized they can usually be dealt with rationally and removed as resistance to trance induction.

Hypnotism is a tool of medical science. The hypnologist can never seek to stand alone. To do so would be just as futile as an X-ray or laboratory technician attempting therapy. A hypnologist's subject should always be under the care and observation of a physician.

Should the physician be the hypnologist? Here, too, the comparison with the X-ray and laboratory technicians is valid. Certainly the physician can have all the training and skill needed to encompass these supplemental functions in addition to his diagnosing and treating. But it would be a waste of his precious time at the expense of his patients were he not to rely instead on these specialists.

The induction and management of the state of hypnosis is no less intricate a science than that practiced by the X-ray and laboratory technicians. And it is many times more time consuming. Hundreds of volumes and technical papers have been written on the subject. From them have emerged a number of techniques that are in fairly universal use. How the right technique is selected for the right subject and custom fitted with a modicum of art is the business of the next two chapters.

12

The Science and Art of Induction

Hypnosis begins for the subject long before he arrives at the hypnologist's office. The all-important ingredients of confidence, expectation, and belief have been building up. Without any of these he might just as well not ring the bell. With all three, he is a prime subject and hypnotism will very likely work its blessings for him.

When a nurse in a physician's office conducts an initial interview with a new patient, she records important data for the doctor on hereditary characteristics and previous medical history. When the hypnologist has an initial interview with a patient, he will very likely conduct it himself, for this preliminary step can also contribute to confidence, expectation, and belief, and he wishes to get the most mileage from it.

The initial interview also provides the hypnologist with some revealing information about the subject, information which helps the hypnologist to understand the subject's degree of suggestibility, the existence of any mental blocks to the hypnotic process, and possibly even the type of induction method most likely to succeed.

The hypnologist's office is the epitome of comfort. There is a choice of upholstered or hard-back chairs and a couch for subjects who prefer the supine position. The temperature is just right, possibly a little on the warm side. There are no drafts. There is indirect lighting which can be dimmed or raised. There are no street noises audible and sounds from the waiting room or adjacent areas are muffled.

There are no gadgets in view. There may be a metronome standing on a small side table. A few pictures hang on the wall. A visitor may not notice that two of the walls have small black discs about four feet off the floor. There may be some interesting gadgets tucked away out of sight. We'll soon find out more about them.

The Initial Interview

When the subject sits down alongside the hypnologist's desk, the hypnologist already knows why he is there from a phone conversation, and has spoken to the subject's physician. A few sympathetic questions about the condition now serve to provide the hypnologist with a chance to observe the subject at close hand. It also serves to remind the subject of the conditions that he would like to get rid of, stimulating his motivation. To make the cheese more binding, he is asked if he really wants to get over his difficulties. This permits him to vocalize a suggestion to himself and set the stage for more to come.

"Do you enjoy reading or going to the movies?" The question may come as a surprise to the subject. "Why, yes, why do you ask?" The hypnologist explains that how the subject reacts to movies and books is helpful in evaluating him as a subject. Does he laugh boisteriously? Weep in the sad spots? Does he forget about his surroundings when the interest gets high? Such deep involvement can signal a good subject.

"Have you ever been hypnotized before?" Any prior experience with hypnosis can be helpful to the hypnologist. What method was used? Did it work? If it did, chances are it will be the most likely method to try again. To change might be to risk destroying a high level of expectation that the subject now has. This expectation can be built upon and a good state of hypnosis can result, even better than the previous experience he remembers.

If there has been no prior experience with hypnosis, or if there has been only superficial experience, such as viewing a stage hypnotist perform, this is where the hypnologist attempts to remove the fears, misconceptions, and resistance. No, it is not dangerous. Yes, you can be hypnotized —everybody can be hypnotized. No, you do not have to be weak-minded. No, nobody will control your will. Yes, you will remember everything that happens.

The atmosphere has now been prepared for the first suggestibility tests. "I am going to ask you to visualize some simple mental pictures. This visualization is helpful to hypnosis. For instance, if you visualize a sizzling steak smothered with onions, your salivary glands will be activated. Your mouth will water. Were I to give you the suggestion that your mouth will water, it would not have anywhere near the effectiveness of this visual image. Are you ready?"

Actually, ready or not the test is over. The subject will already have swallowed as the image of a sizzling steak flashed through his mind. That swallow, or its lack, was observed by the hypnologist.

"First I would like you to visualize a car. Got it? Now a book. Okay? Scotch tape. Now adhesive tape. Imagine a strip of adhesive tape across your forehead. What would happen now if you were to visualize it over your eyes?"

This last question has purposely been worded cautiously. Were the hypnologist to suggest the image of eyes taped over, and the eyes did not close, it would be an obvious failure. The purpose of this whole series of mental images would then have been easily seen to be eye closure. Failure at this point could interfere with the expectation of the subject. He would then expect failure, not success. The hypnologist must treat similarly every step of the way. If failure comes, only the hypnologist can know.

Seeking the proper path to hypnosis for a subject dare not be a case of "Well, we've tried that one and it doesn't work, let's try another." This builds up the failure factor and the hypnologist is literally then working against himself. It is the success factor that needs to be built up, even if by trickery.

If the eyes close temporarily, or blink, visualizing the adhesive over them, the subject is ready for the first induction attempts. Trickery even now can help. At the first sign of a blink, the operator must predict that it will happen. "You may find that your eyes will blink (or close). See! They just did. This is a good sign." Now the subject is convinced he can be hypnotized, in fact that he *is* being hypnotized.

Susceptibility Tests

The subject who blinks or closes his eyes during a tape image exercise is ready for one of the eye closure induction methods that will be described later. If the subject does not react, the door is open for further testing—each presented in such a way that failure is not inferred and the door is left open for the next.

"One of the keys to hypnosis is relaxation. How well do you relax? Let me just see. Now as I lift your hand gently toward your face you will relax. The closer your hand gets to your face, the more relaxed you will become." The hypnologist raises one of the subject's hands slowly. Good subjects will close their eyes one fourth of the way. They are then ready for the hand levitation method of induction.

If no signs of relaxation occur, additional susceptibility tests are needed. The postural sway test is one that is universally used. The subject is asked to stand. The hypnologist stands behind him. "I am going to place my hands gently on your shoulders. I want you to image that there is a magnetic force in them that pulls you back toward me. Do not be afraid of falling. I will support you as you are drawn back. Can you feel the pulling? It is making you fall back!"

Some hypnologists have a machine that measures the resulting sway. A string attached to the subject's shoulder activates a dial. However, it is not needed, as any noticeable sway is significant. It is the noticeable resistance that signals the need for further search for the cause of resistance or the need for further tests.

The shopping bag test is also in general use. It is especially effective in group hypnosis sessions. "Raise both arms so that they extend horizontally in front of you. Now close your eyes gently and imagine that I have hung a shopping bag over your left arm at the wrist. The shopping bag is full and quite heavy. You can hardly hold up your arm. Gradually your arm begins to lower."

Most subjects will demonstrate a gradual deflection of

the arm to some degree, the greater the better. A rigid arm indicates continued resistance.

The handclasp method used by the stage hypnotist in the previous chapter is also a method used by clinical hypnologists. So is the pendulum test described for use in self-hypnosis.

If resistance to hypnosis exists, it very likely cannot be attributed to so-called personality traits. For decades researchers have attempted to correlate personality factors with susceptibility or resistance to hypnosis. Some claimed to have found a correlation between extroverted types and susceptibility. Others could find no such correlation. In 1931 M. Baumgartner reported in the *Journal of Applied Psychology* that he found a positive correlation with tactfulness and honesty, and a slight negative correlation with optimism. Later, S. Rosenzweig and S. Sarason found hypnotizability associated with repression. Apparently the use of this repression by the subject as a mechanism of defense indicated susceptibility.

No clear-cut correlations have emerged from any of these studies. The only common ground of agreement is in the truism that the motivations to be hypnotized must outweigh the motivations not to be hypnotized. Most persons have inner secrets they fear will be divulged once they are hypnotized. Factors such as these must be neutralized and the urge to be rid of uncomfortable symptoms must be built up before an induction method can be found to be effective.

Inducing the Trance State

Based on his observation during susceptibility tests, the hypnologist selects one of several accepted induction methods. He may or may not begin induction at the first session. It all depends how well matters have progressed. He may deem it advisable to proceed slowly and remove some of the subject's reservations before continuing.

Assuming the subject is ready, the induction begins. One popular technique is the relaxation method. The patient is seated comfortably in a straight-back chair. He is questioned about his being thoroughly comfortable. Perhaps another chair would be better for him. Once ready, the monologue proceeds basically as follows:

"I would like you to relax and feel some of the sensations that relaxation brings. Make yourself comfortable, sit loosely, limply. Now you take a point on the ceiling, perhaps where the wall and the ceiling meet, and once you have picked that point just keep staring at it. Look at it. Don't strain, just effortlessly look at the point. Soon you will notice that your eyelids will become tired, and heavy. I want you to take slow deep breaths. Slow and deep. You will begin to feel this feeling of relaxation. You will begin to feel the feeling of heaviness. You notice that your eyes are beginning to blink now. Good, it's one of the signs that you are becoming relaxed. This relaxation will seem to spread all throughout your body. Notice that it will begin with your feet, becoming heavy, and the heaviness will creep into your ankles, into your thighs, your whole body will become heavy with relaxation. With every breath that you take your body is becoming more and more relaxed, and the heaviness is creeping into your chest, into your arms, and down into your hands. Even the small muscles in your face become relaxed. Around your forehead, and your eyes, around your cheeks, and your mouth and your jaws.

"Your eyes seem to want to close now. Don't try to keep them open. Let them do what they want to do. Let them relax. Let them close. Once they close, just keep them closed. Now that your eyes are closed, visualize a wall. This wall is as far as you can see, as high as you can see. It is all one color. There is nothing to look at. Just empty your mind of thoughts. Think of nothing, just relax. Breathe slowly and deeply. Just as though you were pretending that you were asleep. With each breath just go deeper and deeper asleep. You are getting very, very close to sleep. Very, very close. You are so relaxed, you no longer feel like doing anything. You don't feel like moving or talking. You have a kind of detached feeling. You are able to ignore all of the outside sounds. Pay attention only to me. You can ignore everything else, as you keep on relaxing and going deeper and deeper into relaxation. With every breath you are becoming more and more drowsy. More and more sleepy. Now you are so relaxed and so drowsy that you can respond to even deeper feelings of relaxation.

"You can respond to a wonderful deep drowsiness which is all that you want to respond to. And as you hear my voice you are able to follow various instructions, and directions, that I may give you."

The subject is now in a hypnotized state. Just how deep the state is can be determined by the hypnologist through observation and testing which will be described later. He is ready for suggestions aimed at accomplishing the purpose of the session. These suggestions, their construction and verbalization, and the management of the hypnotic state will be covered in the next chapter.

There are other induction techniques that can be used. The hand levitation method is very effective. Here is how it goes. Again, the subject is seated in a comfortable chair with the hypnologist seated nearby.

"Now sit comfortably in your chair and place the palms of your hands on your thighs. I want you to look down at your hands. You might find that your attention is directed more to one hand than the other. When this occurs, this is the hand that I want you to watch. The hand that your mind tells you to watch. I want you to be able to relax and in the course of relaxing, I am going to point out some of the things that you might feel, some of the things that you might experience. For example, you will be able to feel the weight of your hand. You might be able to feel the warmth of your hand. And you will notice that your hand is very still. But as you continue watching your hand, you will notice that one of the fingers of your hand seems to attract attention more than the others. It might be the thumb or the little finger. It might be the index finger or any finger, but one of your fingers will have a desire to move and as you concentrate and relax you will begin to feel this desire building up in one of your fingers. There you see the movement in your little finger, and as you watch it the sensation gets stronger and stronger and you can feel your finger moving and as your finger moves, you will be ready for the next change, the next sensation. You begin to feel a desire that your fingers want to spread apart or perhaps lift up and your fingers will become lighter and lighter. This lightness will extend into all of your fingers, until you will notice that your hand is no longer pressing on your leg. There is less and less pressure. Your hand is hardly touching your leg. You keep watching your hand. Watching it become lighter and lighter. Watching it begin to lift up and you can feel yourself relaxing more and more. You begin now to feel a heaviness in your

eyes, a heaviness, and your hand will begin to lift toward
your face. Your hand continues this lightness, and you feel
yourself becoming drowsy and sleepy.

"Soon you will feel like closing your eyes and feeling
these sensations even more strongly. Now your hand is
lifting higher, lifting higher and higher. Your hand is
lifting closer and closer to your face. And the closer your
hand comes to your face the drowsier and sleepier you
become. Your hand is lifting up and up. Your whole body
is in a deep state of relaxation. Your eyes are closed now,
but in your mind you can still see your hand lifting up
and up toward your face. Now your hand is touching your
face. You are in a deep state of relaxation. You will
listen . . ."

The author has developed some methods that are singu-
larly effective with certain subjects. Where a less permissive and more authoritarian approach is indicated, the
following induction method is quite successful. The seated
subject is asked to hold his or her arms horizontally forward, level with the shoulder, and then to concentrate on
the left hand.

"Now just watch your hand, keep your eyes on your
hand. Soon your arm is going to become heavy and tired.
And soon your arm is gradually drifting down and as your
arm drifts down you will become drowsy and sleepy. As
your eyes follow your hand down, you will become more
and more drowsy and when your hand touches your leg
you will be in a deep, relaxed sleep. And notice how your
hand now begins to feel heavy and how this heaviness
stretches into your arm and into your shoulder and how
relaxed your body is becoming. You will breathe deeply
and with each breath your arm will become heavier and
heavier and as your arm drifts down and down and as
your eyes become heavier and heavier you become more
and more attentive to my voice. You ignore everything
else, everything around you. Your hand is halfway down
now to your leg. You are becoming more and more
drowsy. Your hand is going down and down. Now your
eyes are closing, but your hand continues to go down and
down, and when your hand touches your leg that will be
your signal to immediately go into a deep and profound
sleep. Your body will become limp and heavy. You will
feel wonderful. You will feel so drowsy and sleepy, nothing

will bother you. Now your hand is ready to touch your leg. Now sleep."

One method that the author has developed has proved extremely rapid whenever it can be used. The patient sits in a chair, feet flat on the ground, hands in lap. The hypnologist sits directly in front facing the subject. He puts his hands on the subject's wrists.

"Please look down at your left hand, breathe deeply. Now with every breath that you take I will lift your hand a little toward your face. I am beginning to lift your hand now and as I do so you will be able to imagine the distance between your hand and your face as a distance between waking and sleeping for as I bring your hand up closer and closer to your face, you will begin to relax deeply and float nearer and nearer to sleep. You're becoming drowsier now as I lift your hand, drowsier and drowsier. Your eyes are getting tired and drowsy, tired and sleepy, your eyes are getting heavier and heavier. Soon your eyes will close. Now your hand is almost to your face. Your shoulders are beginning to relax, your neck is beginning to relax, your head becomes heavier and heavier and wants to drift down toward your hand, your head wants to drift down toward your hand. Now your eyes are closed. When your hand touches your face, you will be completely relaxed, completely relaxed, completely relaxed."

This induction method can take as little as two minutes. It has proved very expedient and the author uses it quite frequently.

The four monologues presented so far have progressed in authoritarian quality. The words "you may" and "you might" give way to "you will." Instead of "It might be interesting for you to notice that as you relax, your legs seem to get heavier," your authoritarian approach becomes "Your legs are heavier." Skillful hypnologists are trained in a variety of techniques. It is often necessary to switch from one to another in midstream where resistance is present. This must be done in such a way that never is the suspicion of failure present. Rather must belief and expectation be intensified.

Special Induction Techniques

Induction methods can be placed into four general categories: permissive, authoritarian, confusing, and mechanical.

J. G. Watkins is credited with the development of a postural-sway method that places the subject in a trance state while standing. The hypnologist stands at the side of the subject facing his profile. The instructions then proceed along these lines:

"Put your heels and toes together. Stand erect, shoulders back. Good. Now breathe easily and close your eyes. I want you to imagine that your feet are clamped to the floor, but you are free to sway as a tree would in the wind. You can move back and forth. You are already beginning to feel unsteady. You move slowly forward, then back. Now don't try to do anything. Just let yourself sway. Don't worry, I will not let you fall.

"Now you are beginning to move forward ever so slightly. Now backward. You lean gently forward, then lean gently backward. It is a pleasant motion."

The hypnologist times his remarks to coincide with the sway and just like swinging a child, a periodic encouragement begins to affect the total arc of the sway. His tone is monotonous and has an element of pleading in it. This changes to a more dominant tone as the swaying increases. And instead of following the sway, the hypnologist leads it.

The depth of the trance state can be increased at this point by increasing the volume of the voice so that commands produce a more rapid and violent swaying. Finally, the subject is induced to fall backward by emphasizing that word and minimizing the word "forward": "You are swaying forward, you are swaying *backward*." The word "swaying" is then replaced with the word "falling" and the subject will then fall over backward in a deep trance. He is caught by the hypnologist and eased into a chair.

The subject who does not reach a deep state of trance by this method catches his own fall by taking a step backward or by putting his hands back on the waiting chair. This is the tip-off that only a light state has been attained.

The subject who continues to sway but does not fall is probably apprehensive and may need to be reassured that the hypnologist will support him. This is done by the hypnologist placing his hand on the subject's back to suggest support.

A technique known as the confusion method is an interesting one. The subject tends to withdraw from reality because it becomes too complex to understand. Here is the way it might go (the subject is seated):

"As I will talk to you, you will notice a relaxed drowsiness and sensation of relaxation and as you get relaxed and as you become relaxed you might remember it was a very pleasant day on a Saturday in August of last year, that you were stretching in your garden and relaxing, allowing your head to relax and your eyes to close, and many other summer days, and in spring and in fall. And there were Mondays and Tuesdays in 1951 and 1953 and you are reminded that some evenings when the sun was low that you had a quiet dinner on a Saturday or on a Sunday. It is hard to remember as you were sleeping soundly and deeply, remembering that you were sleeping soundly. And what were you thinking about on those summer days, as you felt sleepy, and relaxed . . ."

There is no sense to it except that it is an attempt to confuse the mind and at the same time to introduce a continuous feeling of relaxation.

The confusion and postural sway techniques can be combined. The operator places his hands on the subject's shoulder and induces a circular sway. He is asked to count backward from 100 to zero and not to pay attention to the hypnologist's voice. Then comes the nonsense monologue. This can also be combined with hand levitation. The three-way technique can be highly effective and rapid.

Induction with Mechanical Aids

Just as a light or a spot on the wall aids hypnotism, so can other objects serve to sidetrack the conscious mind. Twirling objects that reflect light and spinning wheels are more the tools of the amateur who needs a substitute for technique than they are aids to the clinical hypnologist.

Occasionally, however, these mechanical aids do serve a purpose. This is illustrated by the coin technique in which the methods outlined above are accelerated with a nickel or a quarter. The subject is asked to hold the coin clenched in his fist and extend his arm forward.

"Keep your eyes on your thumb as you hold your arm forward at eye level. When you complete the instructions I give you, you will go into a state of deep relaxation. It is very simple. Keep looking at your thumb as I explain what is about to happen. I am going to count to three. When I get to the count of three, you are to open your fist and close your eyes. When you hear the coin hit the floor that will be the signal to you that you cannot open your eyes and that you are in a welcome, refreshing state of relaxation. Are you ready? All right, *one*, remember you do just two things. Open your fist and close your eyes. *Two*, when the coin hits you will be deeply relaxed. *Three!* Straighten out your fingers stiff and rigid and you will become even more relaxed. Now you are very deeply relaxed."

The coin technique has many variations. It can be done with the eyes closed. It can be extended over a longer count. It can be combined with confusion patterns to overcome resistance and through sheer mental exhaustion, cause the subject to accept the state of hypnosis.

The hypnologist's eyes can aid the process of induction. The hypnotic eye has come to be synonymous with the "evil eye" and has acquired a social taboo. However, in the framework of hypnotherapy where consent of the subject is an ever-present factor, and removal of an unwanted physical or mental condition an ever-present goal, prejudice such as this steps aside.

The hypnologist is seated on a stool facing the subject about one foot away, and on eye level with him. "Now look in my eyes. Don't focus on the bridge of my nose or on one eye or the other. Keep your gaze fixed on my gaze as you think of nothing but sleep. That's right, keep looking. Your eyelids are beginning to feel heavy. You will soon want to close them. Your eyes are closing now. Close them!" If the subject does not respond to the authoritarian command, additional time will be needed for heaviness suggestions. The skilled operator will hold off on the command until a fluttering of the lids indicates that the subject is on the brink and can be shoved over with the right dominant approach.

Contrary to popular understanding, while the subject stares into the hypnologist's eyes, the hypnologist is not staring back. He is actually focusing his own eyes on the bridge of the subject's nose, where the gaze is not returned and an unfettered scope of observation can be maintained.

Often the subject does not close his eyes even on command but is still in a satisfactorily deep state of hypnosis. This can be due to a rigid fixation which is easily overcome by the operator's gently closing the subject's lids, as he continues with suggestions for deep relaxation.

Getting back to gadgetry, before hypnotism became a

science, the use of hand pressure, the fixed gaze, and more generally unusual and intriguing objects were the order of the day. In the middle of the nineteenth century, Dr. Esdaile used what was called a magnetizer. A piece of metal brought light pressure to the subject's stomach. James Braid was among the first to use a bright object held a few inches from the subject's gaze. He recognized that converging the patient's eyes into a concentrated focus and misdirecting his attention removed all thought of possible failure and helped the suggestion of relaxation and sleep.

Fatigue being a natural preliminary to sleep, eye fatigue through the need to stare becomes a natural preliminary to responding to sleep suggestions. Hence there were developed such objects as that credited to Dr. Luy, which consisted of a rotary mirror. It was formed by many tiny specks of glass glued into the many faces of a wooden frame. The surfaces of these glass specks produced a dazzling effect as the object was revolved. Successors to this device are as varied as the inventive human mind: whirling discs with intriguing circular designs, pendulums with mirrors, flashing lights. A simple hourglass is popular. Spiral patterns, concentric rings, expanding and contracting circular shapes—all give the subject an attention-compelling diversion.

Perhaps the ultimate development for the objective school of induction is the so-called "brain wave synchronizer" that emits a special controllable pattern of light. It has received wide publicity in medical and hypnosis journals and is also advertised in consumer publications for use in self-hypnosis.

Color is often used effectively. The color contrast method utilizes a gray cardboard with light yellow and light blue color patches separated by a slit. As the subject holds the card and concentrates on the slit the operator predicts he will see additional colors appear and that this will be a sign of hypnosis. Actually the other colors do appear to everybody as respective complementary colors along the outside of the strips. Not knowing that this is a normal phenomenon, the subject's confidence and belief in his own susceptibility takes a giant step forward.

But not all mechanical assistance is optical. The classic metronome is an effective auditory aid to induction. Set to fifty beats a minute and muffled in a cabinet it does its best work. Sound machines are marketed from time to

time. The hum of a faradic machine was once a common
road to induction through auditory stimulation. Sound recordings of the human voice and other noises are in use
today for both hypnosis and self-hypnosis. A small microphone has been used to amplify the subject's heart or
respiratory sounds which he then listens to through
earphones.

Hypnosis by Passes and Pressures

The objective, as opposed to the straight suggestive or subjective, method has often been implemented without the
use of objects through the use of motions and applications
of the hands. Passes of the hands were originated by the
mesmerists as affecting the field of animal magnetism.
Today, a theatrical effect is the chief cause of their survival. This is valid to the extent that this effect stimulates
the subject's induction through his own belief in them.

Major types of passes in use in the past included longitudinal passes made from head to foot with the hand a
few inches from the body, and circular passes usually
made in front of the face. In his book on regression published in France in the mid-1920s, A. De Rochas found
that longitudinal passes brought about spontaneous regression. He therefore used this method where regression was
a goal of the therapy. Passes have survived among professional practitioners today as an adjunct to subjective
methods for a number of reasons, chief of which is that
why should any tool be dropped as long as there are
subjects who respond to one tool and not to another?

The hypnotist can use his hands to apply pressure on
various parts of the body as an induction aid. These pressures are, of course, accompanied by suitable suggestion.
For instance, the thumb and forefinger of one hand is
placed on the bridge of the patient's nose, while the fingers
of the other hand press against the back of the neck at its
base. With both hands exerting mild pressure, there is a
tendency for the head to tilt backward ever so slightly. "I
am now pressing on special nerves that induce sleep. When
I release my fingers, you will fall back and be in a deep
relaxed sleep." The fingers on the nose remain a fraction
of a second longer than the fingers on the neck. In this
instant, unnoticed by the subject, the pressure tilts the

head back forcibly thus causing apparent conformance to the suggestion. Once again belief goes to work and hypnosis is induced.

Hypnosis and Drugs

It has never been shown conclusively that a drug can induce a hypnotic state in itself. Nor has it been demonstrated that any pharmaceutical agent can cause an increase in suggestibility that can be likened to hypnosis. Therefore there is no such thing as drug hypnosis.

However, there are drugs that cause an increase in waking suggestibility and are consequently a useful adjunct in the initial stages of standard methods of induction. Just how they act is not fully understood but it is believed that their success is not due to any actual opening of the mental pores of suggestibility, but rather the removal of negative, inhibiting attitudes.

There is also the possibility that these drugs decrease the capacity for conscious volition or critical judgment, and thus prepare the subject for the induction process of dissociation of awareness.

The effect of alcohol on suggestibility is popularly recognized. Barbiturates are known to have the same effect. One of these—sodium pentothal—was introduced in World War II by two U. S. Army psychiatrists, Drs. Grinker and Spiegel,[1] who were able to obtain a narcotic state similar to verbally induced hypnosis. Pentothal's acceptance has been widespread among many physicians who seek an easily attained hypnotic state for their patients. It is also helpful in the induction of a narcohypnotic state in persons who could not otherwise be hypnotized such as mutes, psychotics, and the emotionally disturbed.

There is no doubt that pentothal does produce a deep trance in a matter of moments without a word of monotonous verbalizing. But there is considerable doubt that such a state permits the effective use of suggestion. Furthermore, it occasionally causes violent reactions, and bad side effects place it in the same category as ether, paraldehyde, chloroform, and the host of other drugs tried in the past and shelved. Add to this list Medinal, Amytal, and Evipal—all with a record of successful use in difficult

[1] *War Neuroses*, by R. Grinker and J. Spiegel, Blakiston, Philadelphia, 1945.

cases, but a use that is best limited to pre-induction conditioning.

In summarizing, any induction method is a good method if it results in a satisfactory state of true hypnosis. Where methods fail, it is usually because the hypnotist has tried to fit the patient to the method, rather than the method to the patient. Where a method recognizes the patient's knowledge, personality, and educational and cultural background, it will have the desired effect on him. If it is totally outside the area of his experience, he will not be able to relate to it, and it will very likely not have the desired effect on him.

A good hypnologist never adopts one method for habitual use despite its index of success. Methods must vary as circumstances vary. Just what will capture the subject's attention and fire his imagination—this is the great determining factor.

Once the induction method has been successfully selected and implemented, the hypnologist has before him a human being who has opened his subconscious mind. There he sits. A man who needs help desperately. There she sits. Everything else has been tried; this is her last hope. How the hypnologist manages the state he has induced, deepening it where necessary, utilizing the suggestibility it has brought about, and terminating it—this is the crux of the whole process and is described in the next chapter.

13

The Science and Art
of Managing Hypnosis

The power of the spoken word is never so manifest as when directed to a hypnotized person. Speech is the quickest way to the human brain, but when it reaches the brain of a person in hypnosis, its message strikes deep within the very life force, instantly.

The nature of suggestion is such that it becomes a thought message that provokes change. It brings about a mental or emotional response. Telling a hypnotized subject makes it so—at least in his mind and in his body which is controlled by his mind. So suggestion becomes the means of hypnotic therapy and control.

Medical records contain cases where suggestions have had a tremendous effect even without the magnifying assistance of hypnosis. A woman committed suicide by swallowing what she thought was carbolic acid. It was actually a mouthwash. The coroner's report disclosed no evidence of physical damage. She was killed by the power of her own suggestion. No one will ever know the depth of her state of self-hypnosis.

Vocalizing suggestions to the hypnotized subject is a great responsibility. It can lead to miracles and it can lead to disaster. The trained hypnologist knows when he is on the trail of the former or on the brink of the latter.

Testing Hypnotic Depth

In the last chapter, the subject was induced into a state of hypnosis through suggestion. He or she is now sitting comfortably in a chair. The hypnotist is seated nearby. Hypnosis exists, but it could be a very light trance or a medium trance. It is necessary for the hypnologist to know how deep a stage has been attained. For, if it is not deep enough to remove the unwanted symptoms or conditions, it must be deepened.

The spoken word is the only tool available to the hypnologist to test for depth. He used this tool for induction; he will use it now to determine how successful that induction has been; and then he will use it for therapy and for terminating hypnosis.

This spoken word has been recorded and published in many books in psychology, psychiatry, hypnosis, and medicine. The verbatim monologues are often used for similar purposes by doctors, psychologists, and others in their own practice when hypnotism is indicated. However, although a good expedient, it is not the best approach, for every person is different, and suggestions must be custom-fitted to the personality. Disaster approaches if a person's defenses are broken down. Miracles appear if a person's experiences are built up.

Caution by the hypnologist at the induction stage was motivated by a desire not to break the subject's confidence in him. Caution by the hypnologist now is motivated by a desire not to say anything that would be of a psychologically disturbing nature. It is also motivated by a desire not to disturb a shaky house of cards on which the very state of hypnosis has been built.

The hypnologist must test for the depth of this stage without permitting an element of failure to enter the subject's mind. An iota of such failure could shake the house of cards and end the state.

For instance, the subject's hands are on the arms of the chair. The hypnologist knows the subject is hypnotized, but he does not know just how deeply. He is about to put out a feeler: "As you become more and more relaxed, I will be able to point out to you certain sensitivities that you might not be aware of. Without opening your eyes, concentrate on the index finger of your right hand."

If the subject is truly hypnotized, there will be a slight twitching of the finger. The hypnologist is quick to confirm this aloud: "There! You felt that involuntary movement of the finger. It demonstrates that you are entering a deeper and deeper state."

If no reaction has occurred, no movement of the finger, the worst thing that the hypnologist could do is divulge his disappointment. The admission of failure would be a powerful suggestion that there was no hypnotic state and that there probably could not be.

Instead, the hypnologist extends his suggestion further: "Can you imagine a fine thread tied around this finger? I have the other end of it and I am tugging on it." If there is still no movement, the hypnologist must give himself a face-saving out. "Can you move your finger to simulate this?" Then a new trick is tried. If the finger has responded to the thread image, then this response can be used to lead into the hand levitation induction technique to deepen the stage.

Another method of testing the depth of hypnosis is in inviting the subject to speak. The sound of his voice is a good indication. The deeper the stage, the weaker and more distant sounding. Here is how this is done. Further relaxation stages are given including suggestions of laziness, drowsiness, a feeling of partial detachment: "You are listening more and more intently to my voice and ignoring all other sounds. You are paying no attention to anything else around you. Every muscle is relaxed, even your vocal cords. If you were to attempt to speak your voice might be weak, as if it were far away, or you might feel it too difficult to speak at all. Now tell me your name."

Note that the hypnologist has given himself leeway. He dare not say, "You cannot speak." Then any use of his voice that the subject would make could end what stage there was. This way, even if he does speak, no harm done. It was expected.

If the voice is weak but a deeper stage is desired, the hypnologist can proceed to utilize other physical movements as follows: "As you relax deeper and deeper, you feel no desire to move or to speak. Your legs and arms are becoming more and more heavy. Your head drifts slightly down to your chest." Here again, failure is ignored, success is exploited. If there is a noticeable lowering of the head, the hypnologist points it out to the subject. If there is not, he goes on to something else. Everything he sees he feeds back to the subject as food for deepening the stage.

Another test is for the hypnologist to place his hand on the subject's hand. "Your arm is weak. Try lifting it." He feels the reaction as the subject's arm moves. If there is complete lethargy, with no perceptible motion, the subject is in a medium trance.

Relative Stages and Their Characteristics

The medium trance, stages fifteen to twenty in the scale of stages described earlier, is when certain physical changes begin to occur. Glove anesthesia exists. A pin can be put through the skin of the finger or hand without pain. Sensory changes can be effected.

In this stage somebody on a salt-free diet can be given the suggestion that food without salt tastes thoroughly seasoned and to add salt would make it taste excessively salty. The whole field of diet control through posthypnotic suggestion begins at this stage. It is the stage, too, where the entertaining hypnotist can pull some of his humorous antics: "This bottle (ammonia) smells just like perfume."

Let's take another look at the subject. He sits there comfortably. His head might sag. He has a heavy look about him. There is no movement, not even a cough, blink, or other involuntary motion. There is no conversation.

It is impossible to tell by observation whether the subject is in an even deeper state of hypnosis than the medium levels. The hypnologist must test. The next deeper state is somnambulism. In this state the subject can open his eyes without affecting the state. The hypnologist will lose ground if he orders the eyes opened and the subject is in only a medium trance state. Instead he examines the eyelids first. He says, "I am going to touch your forehead, but it will not disturb you." He touches the eyelids. There is no reflex. He lifts them up gently. He observes that the eyes are rolled up or inward. He can now proceed safely with the suggestion that the eyes will open and the trance not be affected. The subject opens his eyes. They are fixed straight ahead. They do not wander around the room, nor do they appear to be focused on anything in particular.

Subjects are normally amnesiac in their thirtieth to thirty-fifth stages on the scale. They are not likely to remember consciously any of the suggestions that are given. It is the state required for dental surgery and other operations where good anesthesia is needed. Both the anesthesia and amnesia can be safely tested without labeling it a test. The dentist or surgeon tests by asking the patient to compare sensitivity of the gums or anesthetized areas with other areas. Thus a feeling of some sensitivity will not be tantamount to failure, as it might if measured alone. "I feel your finger less on my right cheek than on my left cheek" tends to support the hypnosis.

To test amnesia, the hypnologist says, "When I count to three you will awaken, but you will not remember the suggestion that I have given you about your smoking. Then when I count backward to one again, you will return to an even deeper state." On the count of three, the subject awakes and can be asked a direct question about remembering references to his not smoking. He can then be placed right back into hypnosis instantly by reversing the count, three, two, one.

The Deepest State

Where deep psychiatric problems are involved in symptom removal, the subject may need to uncover lost memories in order for therapy to be effective. This means age regression, and a state of hypnosis in the fortieth to forty-fifth stages.

An effective aid to deepening the state so as to approach this level is to reassure the subject that as he goes deeper, the hypnologist will be able to awaken him and terminate the session in a split second. In fact should anything happen to the hypnologist, the subject can dehypnotize himself by use of a predetermined arrangement, just as quickly.

The deepening process is again helped by latching on to a physical motion or a mental image. "With every breath you take you can relax into a deeper and deeper state of tranquility. Your breathing gets slower and more regular as you sink into this relaxed state." The hypnologist can time his suggestion to follow the rhythm of chest movement, speaking the words slowly and deliberately.

The hand can be used again, either in levitation as before, or it can be raised and then lowered to the lap. The operator can lift the arm and say, "When I release your arm it will drop to your lap and when it touches your lap you will enter a much deeper state of relaxation."

The experienced hypnologist can get a confirmation of depth from the way the hand falls. If it is lowered slowly, under control, there is still work to be done. If it drops limply with a thud or if it remains suspended without effort, the deep stage has probably been reached. It will be tested some more as the hypnologist goes about its utilization.

The subject will now accept anything that is suggested to him as if it were real. Negative and positive hallucinations can be produced at will. "There are six other people in the room now. I want you to meet them." These six people will exist for the subject just as surely as if they were seated there. People can be removed from the room for the subject as easily as they are apparently brought there. Bring in a tiger, if you will, or a brass band.

Most important in therapy, the clock can be turned back. The subject can be given the year, the time, the place, or asked to set it himself, and then asked to tell what is happening. "What is your father saying?" "What do you reply?" "What else is happening?" These questions will be answered vividly and in many cases will indicate the path further questioning should take in order to elicit information which the psychiatrist, psychologist, or hypnologist feels is important to a solution.

Reaching the fortieth stage or beyond also opens the way for the regulation of bodily functions by direct command. Heartbeat can be regulated, blood pressure controlled. These are important measures in treatment for cardiovascular disorders.

A man with high blood pressure (180) has the gauge around his arm. His physician is present, ready to work the gauge. The hypnologist speaks: "Your blood pressure will return to its normal pattern. You will be extremely relaxed. You will be able to function normally without stress or strain." The physician squeezes the bulb and watches for the reading. The reading is 140.

Less dramatic, but no less welcome by patients, are the

changes that can be effected in the intestinal tract: "You will be able to eliminate normally and naturally when you first arise in the morning and again when you are about to retire at night." Or: "Your body will be able to digest its food in a perfectly normal fashion. You will no longer be troubled by ——" (here the patient's own description of his symptoms is used).

In some cases, it helps if a patient has prior knowledge of how the body works. He is better able to visualize corrective suggestions, and this visualization is often important to hypnotic curative results. Take the case where a hypnologist was called in by a dental surgeon who had just removed a tooth using hypnotically attained anesthesia and was faced with a rare case of "dry socket." This is where the gums do not bleed after an extraction, thus risking an uncleansed condition and slowing up the healing process. The hypnologist told the patient to visualize the socket as it was—dry. Then he said, "You now see the blood beginning to flow. It is pouring forth." And so it was—a real gusher.

The control of blood-coagulation timing is also possible through similar command suggestions, where this factor of the blood is slow and hemorrhaging results.

The results are weird. It is like talking to a master mind that exerts the control.

Popular Suggestive Therapy

Somewhere between light trance states and the ultimate state described above are the intermediate states of hypnosis where most of today's treatment is given. Behavior patterns involving habit, emotion, and attitude control fall into this area. Much has already been said about these suggestions in previous chapters, but it would be well to point out the general nature of suggestions, so that their characteristics can be applied to specifics.

Suggestions to change behavior patterns are usually based on the step-by-step approach toward a desired goal. Take fears or phobias. They are usually brought on by a traumatic experience in the past. It can be treated with psychoanalysis or hypnoanalysis, wherein the original experience and attitude is uncovered and brought to the conscious level, where it is dissolved. Or, if time and money dictate a shortcut, direct suggestions can be given, one step at a time, to counteract the original phobia-producing suggestion of an earlier day. Suppose the phobia is directed at dogs. The patient is a door-to-door salesman and the fear of dogs is interfering with his livelihood. The first suggestion is to visualize a friendly dog he once knew. He pats it. He knows it is a loving dog. He sees he is not afraid. The next suggestion dramatizes this further. He remembers other instances where dogs have been friendly. One licks his hand. He pets it. After several of these visual dramatizations he visualizes a dog he never saw before. It reminds him of all the other friendly dogs he has known. He is not afraid. And so the attitude of non-fear is suggested to replace the fear and it usually does in one or two sessions.

Another characteristic of behavioral suggestions is the personal choice. A woman is faced with problems brought on by excessive gambling. She seeks help through hypnotism. Once induced, she is asked to visualize two paths. On one path lies her present life—her savings disappear, her family is deprived of essentials, her relationship with her husband is strained. On that path lies family bankruptcy and unhappiness. On the other path, there is a life without gambling. It is a happy family life free of monetary problems and blessed with harmony. Which path does she choose? She visualizes herself taking the second path. She sees herself leaving gambling behind and embarking on a happier road.

This two-path suggestion is very effective in many social problems, but has only limited application in symptom removal. Combined with a step-by-step approach, lives have been changed for people with unwanted habits or those who suffer from restricting inhibitions, anxieties, and lack of confidence. First the subject visually selects the path that is devoid of the unwanted factor. Next, he visualizes the first step on the path—a step requiring less fear and more confidence. These visualizations are made at the suggestion of the hypnologist: "You now see yourself . . . etc." They lend themselves to effective use in self-hypnosis.

In the creation of new abilities and the improving of old ones, the two-path and step techniques also prevail, liberally reinforced with appropriate visualizations—e.g., the golfer visualizes a big hole and small ball.

Obesity, insomnia, bed-wetting, thumb sucking, irritability, claustrophobia, menstrual pain, nervousness—all are areas where suggestions reprogram the subconscious to more desirable conditioned behavior. These suggestions follow the same principles, differing only on the specifics and how these are adapted to the subject's own experience. (That woman who is afraid of elevators visualizes them larger and roomier.)

Add to these the vast areas of disease and psychosomatic disorders which can either be cured or effectively relieved in hypnosis, and the one or two hours of effort experienced by the operator in inducing hypnosis and deepening the stage are more than amply rewarded.

Terminating the Hypnotic State

The final suggestions in hypnosis are the ones given by the hypnologist to end the state. But before this is begun, it is essential that all previous suggestions given that have a posthypnotic application be neutralized.

Many hypnologists have learned the hard way that it is best to keep a written record of all suggestions given so that they can be checked off as they are neutralized or reversed. For instance, it can remain as a posthypnotic condition. If suggestions have been made that the subject's voice is weak and far away, they must be undone with the suggestion that "Your voice is now completely normal." Less obvious are suggestions made to test depth or to create a desired illusion. If the doctor is present and his presence seems to obstruct the patient's cooperation, the hypnologist may suggest to the subject that the physician has left the room and is not present. On termination, the physician's presence may cause anxiety or mental conflict in the subject. More than one case has been recorded with the "removed" person remaining invisible to the subject on awakening.

Termination suggestions remove the induction suggestions. They replace heaviness, lassitude, and sleepiness with normalcy, refreshment, and wakefulness.

This can be done carefully or less carefully. The careful method is to work in reverse of induction. The hypnologist goes through the same monologue but instead of "more heavy" it is "less heavy" and instead of "more relaxed" it is "more awake."

The less careful, and faster, method is done by a countdown. The suggestion is given, "I am going to awaken you as I count from one to ten. With each number you will become more and more awake and refreshed." The countdown would then proceed along these lines:

One. Now you are beginning to enter the stage of wakefulness.

Two. With each number you become more and more awake.

Three. As you awake you will feel completely well and refreshed.

Four. You are beginning to be more awake and alert.

Five, six, seven. You are almost awake. You feel perfectly normal now.

Eight, nine, ten. Wake up!

The operator will notice just how fast to proceed during the countdown as the subject evidences signs of arousing from the trance state. Many subjects will not stir until the count of ten. Others will not even stir then and the final suggestion must be repeated: "Anytime now you may open your eyes and be fully awake." Or the hypnologist may have to be even more insistent: "Wake up now! Wake up now! Wake up now!"

The author has had cases where even this insistence bore no fruit, but has found no cause for alarm. He made some phone calls, did some paper work, and in a few minutes the subject aroused himself out of sheer boredom. The subject is never shaken or even touched. The state of hypnosis is usually so restful and welcome to these subjects that they have a desire to prolong it a few more minutes. There is absolutely no danger of the state being prolonged substantially except in cases of certain psychotic patients who should not have been hypnotized in the first place.

Posthypnotic Reactions

It is often a useful part of the termination procedure to give a posthypnotic suggestion that can be left uncanceled as a test of the effectiveness of therapeutic suggestions that have been given. For instance, "After I wake you, you might feel like lighting a cigarette. You will move the ashtray on the side table nearer to you." Or again, "After I wake you, you will raise your arm and touch your forehead with your hand."

It is interesting to see how some subjects cope with

these suggestions. Some comply involuntarily. This is the best reaction. There will be a natural movement of the ashtray, a flick of the forehead, or a natural shift of chairs. Often the compliance is flamboyant and almost defiant, indicating that the subject is resisting for some reason. It is a much more satisfactory reaction for the subject to raise his arm and brush his hair or tug at his ear than to point his finger and touch his forehead.

Here are three typical reactions to the chair changing suggestion:

1. The subject opens his eyes, gets up, and sits down in the green chair. When asked why he made the change, he replies, "You told me to." This reaction raises some doubt about the effectiveness of the posthypnotic suggestion. It can be in the conscious rather than the subconscious mind, and therefore not producing an "automatic" motivation.

2. The subject opens his eyes and after a brief period of comment on the session suddenly changes the subject: "Do some of your patients sit in that green chair?"

"Sometimes. I ask them to sit wherever they feel most comfortable."

"Can I try it?"

"Surely."

This a fine reaction. It shows normal involuntary behavior, tempered only by social amenities. The posthypnotic suggestion is at work where it belongs—in the subconscious.

3. The subject opens his eyes, remains in his chair but wriggles restlessly. Finally he blurts out, almost in anger, "I know what you told me about that green chair. If you want me to sit there, I'll sit there."

"How do you feel about the chair you're in?"

"It's all right."

"Well, suit yourself."

The topic is dropped, but not for long. The subject is still shifting restlessly.

"I don't have to sit in that chair. That is really ridiculous!"

At this point, it is best to relieve the subject's anxiety.

"Of course you don't. But isn't it wonderful the way posthypnotic suggestion works. Go over and sit in that green chair and see how comfortable and at ease you feel."

The subject welcomes this approach, wastes no time in changing chairs, and settles back comfortably. The fidgeting is over and a relaxed conversation usually ensues about the incident. This subject has been thoroughly conditioned by the posthypnotic suggestion but requires an equal dose of conscious motivation, otherwise a conflict ensues.

What happens days later? Here are the ways some subjects have described their reactions to posthypnotic suggestion:

"I used to be glued to the Coke machine in this restaurant where I work as a waitress. Bread, Coke, bread, Coke, all day long. Now after three hypnosis sessions that Coke machine actually feels hot to me. I feel that the apparatus will burn my fingers. As to the bread, I'll slice it, but I won't eat it. I may even bring a piece up to my mouth out of habit, but my mouth won't open. As I write this, two loaves of garlic bread just went by me."

Another says, "I could hear everything you said. You have a very melodious voice. I felt anxious to follow your instructions. I guess you might say I was susceptible to thoughts you gave me right from the start. Potatoes and pizzas are out. I've eaten apple pie once and felt very guilty, so much so I just could not enjoy it. Once I began to chew chi chi beans knowing they are high in carbohydrates and therefore off my new way of eating. The moment I began to chew them I felt nauseous and had to excuse myself. Do you think my stomach spasms were a way of punishing myself?"

A smoker: "I smoked after my first session—one cigarette. I guess I did not really enjoy it. But because of that one cigarette I guess you'd say it took me two sessions to really stop. It was rough for the first week. I used coffee as a substitute. Instead of my usual three or four cups I drank ten cups a day. I didn't miss the cigarettes but I was nervous and jumpy. I couldn't sit still by myself. For some reason I couldn't talk on the telephone for any length of time. I had to say, 'I'll call you back.' But that's all over now and so is smoking."

Some random comments:

"I was given a muscle relaxer by my neurologist. It made me sick. I broke out into rashes and it did not help my wry neck. In one hypnosis session I felt like a new person."

"I did not like to come out of my first hypnotic session, it was so relaxing. Believe me, it's habit forming."

"I feel that I'm aware in hypnosis, but my eyes seem

tighter shut than usual. Then when it's over I feel I'm just waiting for that last count."

"Your voice sounded low and soothing. My movements seemed automatic. I felt I had such wonderful control over my stiff muscles. I kept thinking—I wish I could stay like this."

Advanced Psychiatric Uses of Hypnosis

The techniques of suggestion in hypnosis have of necessity been simplified to provide a basic understanding of its general use. Hypnotism is being used more and more by psychiatrists and psychologists in hypnoanalysis and hypnotherapy where patients' problems transcend the basic health and behavior problems and move into the area of more complicated therapy requiring almost a rehabilitation of the character structure.

For example, even though hypnosis should not be attempted by a hypnologist on a psychotic subject as a general rule, it may offer benefits when used with the psychiatrist present as a supplement to other treatments. A psychosis renders the individual incapable of adjusting to outside pressures and his own internal demands. Consequently there is a retreat that is characterized by delusions and hallucinations. The patient often reverts to infantile stages of development with strong dependency manifestations. When that dependency is broken, as by the death of the person on whom dependency was fixed, the psychosis is acute. Hypnosis can help by substituting another dependency relationship—on the psychiatrist. Once the psychiatrist can make contact with such person, hypnotism can help to consolidate this interpersonal relationship until the ego has been sufficiently strengthened. Hypnoanalytic probing is to be avoided during this period, however, as the emotions likely to be released in the process may prove too much of a burden for the already overburdened ego.

Even with a manic-depressive psychosis, hypnotism is helpful, albeit to a very limited degree. Obviously it is impossible to induce hypnosis during manic stages because of the distracted state of the patient. However, hypnosis can aid in the handling of some of the milder spells of depression. Suggestions of relaxation are given posthypnotically to ease the cycles of the disorder and also suitable suggestions are given to improve self-esteem and self-confidence.

Severe melancholy that often comes to women in their late forties or men in their late fifties is a psychotic condition known as involutional melancholia. There can be such extreme depression and acute misery that the patient often attempts to escape it through suicide. Endocrine gland changes in the body and their effect on sex potency reinforce the feeling that the best of life is over. Here again psychic probing or analysis, with or without hypnosis, is avoided because the problem is not to stimulate the emergence of material from the subconscious, but rather to inhibit it. Instead, hypnotism can be used in mild or incipient cases to induce relaxation and to direct the patient away from a fixation of attention on his symptoms of aging and instead toward a concentration on hobbies, recreation, and occupational therapy.

Hypnosis can be quite harmful in cases of schizophrenia, especially if the patient is asked to recall traumatic experiences of the past, or if posthypnotic suggestions are directed toward doing things which the subject finds terrifying. However, the use of hypnosis can be helpful in attaining relaxation and improving sleep capabilities in these subjects. Suggestions of reassurance and gentle persuasion are also effective and usually without danger.

More Common Psychiatric Applications

The psychiatrist's practice is devoted more to patients with neuroses than to those with psychoses. Here the use of hypnotism becomes remarkably effective to accelerate reassurance, persuasion, guidance, and reconditioning necessary for improvement.

The benefit seems to be threefold. First, a feeling of rapport and confidence so necessary to psychobiologic therapy is accelerated. Second, the patient is convinced that something of an immediate and constructive nature is being done for him. Third, hypnosis acts as a catalyst for positive suggestions and dream analysis used in therapy.

Psychotherapeutic methods that include guidance and advice are aided by hypnosis. Often an authoritarian approach is utilized by the hypnologist for the neurotic person who feels totally helpless. Then as the person is more free of his turmoil and better able to solve his problems, the approach becomes more permissive so as to encourage the development of self-reliance and ultimately self-fulfillment.

Many persons suffering from neuroses respond to reassurance. An understanding attitude on the part of the counselor goes a long way toward arming guidance with the necessary confidence and respect to equate it with reassurance. Reassurance dispels fear. But since fear resides in the subconscious, hypnotism is used to bring about reassurance through the negation of the fear.

Suggestions toward this end are directed at correcting the false ideas, irrational thinking, and fantasies cooked up, exaggerated, and etched in the subconscious. Reassurance given to the subject in a state of hypnosis is accepted more readily and acted upon more vigorously than the same given in a waking state.

Mental persuasion remains as the chief force in relieving patients of neurotic symptoms. This persuasion is along the lines of appealing to reason and intelligence to convince the patient of the false concept he has of his own illness and how this mental concept is bringing about the very illness feared.

All of this can be done without hypnotism, but because it involves change in thinking habits it is done much more easily and, in fact, entirely free of will power, through hypnotism. Simple suggestions act as reconditioners in the overcoming of worry habits, the redirection of goals, control of emotions and attitudes, erasing of tensions and fears, coping with adversity, and rising above physical suffering and disease.

So we have come full circle to accomplish in the hypnologist's office what was described at the outset as the scope of hypnotism today. But like the iceberg that is seen only in small part, the far greater power of hypnotism lies in its promise.

Tomorrow will see hypnotism put to uses that make today's miracles seem bland. The next chapter provides a few glimpses into the potential of hypnotism as it unfolds in the years ahead.

twenty-two .... physicians, dietitians and psycholo-

14

Hypnotism Today
and in the Decade Ahead

Despite the fact that medical journals are constantly reporting new advances made possible with hypnotism, physicians are still largely reticent about proposing hypnotherapy. When asked by a patient about hypnosis and where treatment utilizing hypnosis can be found, they are likely to tell patients that it is dangerous, or that they have no professional confidence in it. Some even make fun of the patient for asking.

Such doctors are fortunate these patients do not seek legal remedy, says Dr. S. J. Van Pelt in a recent issue of the British Journal of Medical Hypnosis. He reminds his colleagues that hypnotism received official recognition and acceptance in 1958 from both the American and British Medical Associations.

This was also the first full year of work by the then newly formed American Society of Clinical Hypnosis, an affiliate of the American Association for the Advancement of Science. Its membership soon grew to over twenty-two hundred physicians, dentists, and psychologists. Only those with a doctoral degree and membership in their respective national professional societies are eligible for membership. Its purpose is to permit various scientific disciplines to exchange information on their knowledge of hypnosis—clinical, experimental, theoretical. It seeks to stimulate research and publication in the field and set up standards of training.

It is difficult to understand how ignorance about hypnotism and its effectiveness in medicine can persist on one street in a town, when around the corner medical men with similar training are utilizing it successfully.

The Progress of Hypnosis in Medical Circles Today

Presumably physicians read their medical journals. They are the chief sources of information on medical advancements and discoveries. Patients are not treated with medicines and therapies dated by the physicians' diplomas and certificates, but with the latest medical science can offer. This is every patient's rightful expectation.

One wonders, though, whether the latest really comes through to these doctors. If the situation with hypnotism is any indication, it often does not. Can you imagine a physician not believing in the wonder drugs, and calling them a passing fancy? Side by side with reports on new drug discoveries are reports on new hypnosis findings. Here are some examples from medical journals in recent years.

Of fourteen patients treated for vision improvement with the help of hypnosis, Kelly reports twelve have an average improvement equivalent of from 20-50 vision to 20-20 vision.

Two patients suffering from premature labor contractions are given suggestions that the contractions will cease. They do and do not reappear until their proper time. A similar report by Schwartz appears a few months later.

Eighteen subjects suffering from asthma and hay fever are divided into two groups of nine each. The hypnotic group is given the suggestion that they will not manifest the skin wheal indicative of this allergy when given the allergy test. In all, there is a smaller weal response and symptoms are correspondingly lessened. So report Fry and Mason.

Minor surgery on 152 men and 132 women is conducted

with hypnosis as the sole anesthetic and found successful for ninety-two percent of the men and ninety-four perc nt of the women. A survey of the patients and surgeons involved reveals that ninety-five percent of the patients with whom it has been used successfully would like to use hypnosis again as an anesthetic if another operation becomes necessary. The surgeons list five advantages: (1) No post-operative pain. (2) Loss of blood is reduced. (3) Recovery time is reduced. (4) Tissue sent to the pathologist for examination is not altered by chemical injection. (5) Time for hypnotic induction is reduced to an average of ten seconds or much less time than required with novocaine. The source is Anatol Milechnin of the Montevideo Medical School.

Flip through the medical journal pages some more. Even if you are a busy doctor and must read fast, you see that Glasser has reduced blood calcium using suggestion in hypnosis, Povovinsky has controlled blood sugar, Langheimrich has changed biliary secretion. Hanson has controlled the secretion of pepsin, trypsin, lipase, diastase. Platonow has caused alcoholic intoxication to completely disappear.

How can physicians not begin to wonder? The answer is probably that their training has never recognized the power of the mind over bodily functions. It is too big a step for them now. A report on a new drug, fine. The discovery of a new surgical technique, great. But when a colleague named Heyer reports in the same journal that using hypnotism he was able to produce a laxative effect with a constipating drug, they throw up their hands!

Improving the Climate for Hypnosis

Recognition of hypnosis as a scientific therapy by the American Medical Association in 1958 was a giant step in improving the professional climate for hypnotism, but there are many giant steps still to be taken if the advantages of hypnotism are to become available to all who stand to benefit from them.

Perhaps the most essential of these steps is the incorporation of hypnotism in the curricula of colleges and medical schools. A check of the largest of these shows that it is not a part of any regular course of study. It is not listed as a course in the catalogues of these institutions, and from inquiries to deans' offices the most that can be ascertained is that occasionally a member of the faculty will include a two- or three-day section on hypnotism, possibly bringing in a guest lecturer for the event.

On the other hand, outside of regular educational channels, a number of privately run schools have been formed which make courses in hypnotism available to any medical disciplines and even lay persons. "Register now for the fabulous eleventh annual convention course" reads an announcement brochure. This particular course was given in Nevada in five days for a fee of two hundred dollars. An eminent faculty of thirteen physicians, dentists, and other professional people covered in depth the history, induction, and management of hypnosis. However, one wonders whether the quickie nature of the course was conducive to a true appreciation of hypnotism as an accepted medical tool by those who heard about the course or attended it.

Many other courses are given by similar schools throughout the year, but they lack the authority that would be accorded them if given by recognized institutions of learning in the medical field. These institutions often sponsor courses such as those offered by the American Institute of Hypnosis, but this makes hypnotism a sort of stepchild in the program rather than a full-fledged segment.

Here is a typical course outline offered by an East Coast group and given under the sponsorship of colleges and universities:

First Day: General orientation—practical screening procedure—authoritarian and permissive suggestibility tests —qualifications of subjects—favorable conditions and contraindications. So-called dangers of hypnosis—indications of possible hysteria—cardiac cases—precautions and contraindications—use of regression—misconceptions—administration of pre-sleep technique and progressive relaxation—how autoconditioning can increase your own professional success—induction techniques—3-step induction procedure—basic methods—frequency and repetition principles—methods of dehypnotization— student practice—stages or levels of hypnosis—practical system for evaluating trance depth—demonstration of additional standard methods—student practice—instruction in self-induction of hypnosis, student participation —second step.

Second Day: Basic induction methods—mechanical aids—
methods of the old masters—types of posthypnotic responses—student practice in induction and evaluation of
trance depth—advanced hypnotic techniques—arm and
hand levitation method—variations in response—student
practice—confusion and distraction techniques—rehearsal method—hypnotic phenomena and their relation
to trance depth—anesthesia management—"instantaneous" methods—indirect (disguised) techniques—relationship to unconsciousness and sleep—demonstration
of waking hypnosis—sensory-motor and placebo techniques—more advanced techniques—eight methods of
deepening hypnosis—evolution of methodology—hypnotic miscellany—controversial aspects—recommended
reading—"instantaneous waking self-hypnosis"—practice—self-hypnosis instruction continued—prehypnotic
suggestion installed, student participation—variations of
technique.

Third Day: Legal and ethical considerations—conflicts
within the professions—applications in medicine generally—case discussions—how you can cure and prevent
emotional depressions—applications. Obstetrics—recommended methods of conditioning for childbirth—problems of vomiting and nausea in pregnancy. Surgery—
methods of maintaining analgesia—combining hypnosis
with chemical anesthesia. Problems in dentistry—alleviation of fear and apprehension—dental hypnoanesthesia
—control of bleeding and salivation—post-operative
healing—adjustment to wearing dental appliances. Obesity. Frigidity, impotence—cancer pain—phantom limb
pain—bed-wetting—nail biting—excessive smoking—
neurodermatitis—psychotherapy and hypnoanalysis.

Note the vast ground covered and the diversity of medical disciplines involved. There is no doubt that the course
can turn out hypnotists in three days, but are they so
versed in the technique after this brief time that they can
handle the multiplicity of problems that arise in subjects?

Psychotherapeutic hypnosis is a specialty in the domain
of psychotherapists and belongs in their regular course of
training leading to licensing or certification. Hypnoanalysis
is another specialty. This one is in the domain of the

psychiatrist and belongs in medical curricula. Other medical hypnosis specialties belong in the academic training of obstetricians, gynecologists, dentists, etc.

Complete acceptance by society would find hypnosis for self-betterment in the domain of educators, and hypnosis for habit control in the hands of other specialists.

A good climate for hypnotism must start with education, not only in special educational seminars, courses, and activities, but also in the regular channels of formal education. Then the classroom can lead to the clinic, to the hospital, to the laboratory, and to the patient who needs it.

Accreditation for Hypnologists

Eventually, with hypnotism understood and taught by educators, and accepted and used in the medical and allied professions, a system of accreditation or licensing could be adopted by the states. At present, there is no way a prospective subject can evaluate the practitioner with a sign on the door. Did he just open after reading a book? Is he a full-time, experienced hypnologist? Or something in between?

The closest a subject can come to checking on a practitioner is to ask for his referral sources. If those referral sources do not include dentists or physicians, the subject will be wise to beat a hasty retreat. If they do, then a call or two to these professionals can quickly ascertain the degree of skill and success of the practitioner.

Accreditation is presently subordinated to other accreditation. Membership in the American Society of Clinical Hypnosis, for instance, is limited to those with a Ph.D. in psychology, an M.D., a D.D.S., or D.M.D. Yet such membership does not imply, much less affirm, skill in applied hypnotism.

The Society has recently formed a foundation, the American Society of Clinical Hypnosis—Education and Research Foundation, which is wrestling with this problem of accreditation, among others. Meanwhile, it has been an excellent force in the establishment of adequate education and instruction in hypnotism to professional people until this type of instruction can be supplied by professional schools.

It conducts periodic workshops, basic and advanced, in

various parts of the country. In the basic workshop are taught and demonstrated the fundamental techniques of clinical hypnosis and their applications to problems of the psychologically normal patient.

The advanced workshop is usually taught by psychiatrists who emphasize the psychosomatic aspects of medicine and dentistry, teach psychotherapeutic principles and techniques, and provide an understanding of the motivations frequently underlying organic symptoms.

Once this type of education is part of standard training, hypnotism will be practiced by skilled professionals rather than professionals with a smattering of exposure to the subject. As a result, it will be practiced more successfully. Every day, somewhere, a patient requests hypnotism and his request is granted by an unskilled professional. Result: Failure. And another spadeful of earth is dug by those who would bury hypnotism. Replace this failure with success after success, which inevitably result from an educated skill, and with each success a brick is laid in the edifice of acceptance.

But another type of educational effort is needed. It is the type of education that the dental assistant receives or the physiotherapist or the X-ray technician. In these cases substantial knowledge of the medical or dental fields is needed but less, of course, than that of the eventual doctor or dentist. The clinical hypnologist knows every technique in the process of susceptibility testing, induction, management, and termination. He provides the physician, dentist, psychiatrist, or psychologist with the time and skill needed to make hypnotism's advantages available to their patients. The accredited hypnologist will only rarely have a blanket accreditation. More often than not his license or certificate will specify his field of practice, excluding hypnoanalysis or other special techniques outside his training.

Time is a major factor in the physician's practice. Many physicians who want to employ hypnotism and who have learned its techniques are not able to put them to use because of time. Ten patients can go through a normal office visit in the time it takes to induce one state of hypnosis in one patient. The clinical hypnologist is needed by the physician as an economic fact of life. He is needed by the dentist and by the psychotherapist for the same reason. This is not only an age of specialization but an age of speed. The stage is set for the emergence of the accredited clinical hypnologist.

The Ideal Clinic for Hypnosis

The next step will inevitably be the formation of clinics for hypnosis. Such clinics will combine various medical specialists, including the clinical hypnologist, in a treatment center where the full effects of hypnosis can adequately be brought to bear on a number of diseases and disorders.

A patient entering such a clinic would first be interviewed by the psychologist to determine whether or not the patient can safely be a hypnotic subject. This is similar to the intake interview in any clinic where eligibility screening must be employed.

Next, the patient moves to the clinical hypnologist who tests for susceptibility, establishes the most appropriate induction method for the subject, and determines the probable maximum trance depth.

The patient then moves on to the specialist that fits the problem—dermatologist, obstetrician, dentist, gynecologist, physiotherapist, psychologist, psychiatrist, etc.—and a program is worked out. The specialist can turn on the state of hypnosis by command due to the previous posthypnotic suggestions implanted by the hypnologist. He need call in the hypnologist only when special techniques are required or when problems arise.

Not only is the hypnologist available for consultation, but these other specialists are also available to each other to discuss the *whole* patient, the all-important doctor-patient relationship, the physiological symptoms, and the psychological symptoms.

No longer will the patient seeking his share of hypnotism's blessings have to turn to the pages of his classified directory and choose between the AAAAA Hypnotism Center and the Miracle Hypnosis Salon, or read the ads to learn how to "hypnotize instantly!" or obtain "secret hypnotic methods." No longer will there be any doubt of where to go and whom to see, of what cannot be done and what can be done.

Today hypnosis is a business. It has no right to be. The author recently learned of a man who went into the business of hypnosis by simply opening an office and advertising. He was an elderly man with no experience. He had read about hypnotism in books. His success in attracting clients was enhanced by the fact that his office was located in a medical center. But there his success ended. He was continuously unsuccessful in his attempts to help people. Consequently those who had contact with him reported the failure of hypnosis to their physicians and others. That is the sad part from the author's point of view, but far sadder indeed were the hopes dashed and therapy that was aborted. Far too many would-be hypnotists are in the business, and one of the tell-tale signs that give them away are the mechanical devices that dot their office. The subject needs something to look at, but a spot on the wall suffices. Elaborate dangles only add a carnival atmosphere. They are a general deception. Few people need the assistance of their attention-holding ability. Hypnotism can well do without these trappings.

Accredited hypnologists working in their private practice with professional referrals or participating in a hypnosis clinic will elevate the judgment that society makes concerning hypnotism in the decades ahead because success will be measured in the proper framework of scientific evaluation. If twelve patients are given sleeping pills, twelve patients sleep and sleeping pills are adjudged successful. But hypnotism is not suitable to all and its success should not be measured on the basis that it is. Used with psychotics, the results can be dismal, with alcoholics better, but not good. Only fifteen percent of serious surgical patients should be selected for hypnosis, whereas as many as eighty percent of obesity cases can respond to hypnosis. According to the author's clinical experiences, depth of hypnosis necessary and the susceptibility of the subject are the determining factors in whether or not hypnotism is an indicated approach. Only where it should the statistics come into play in evaluating and recording success and failure.

Needless to say, hypnotism would then rate much higher and its acceptance would be accelerated in the grass roots of medical practice. The beneficiary would be humanity.

*Some Future Horizons for Hypnotism—
the Psychedelic Experience*

The well-known British psychiatrist Van Pelt reports in a
medical journal that he has had success with the problem
of nagging housewives. He did not treat the wives. Instead
he hypnotized the husbands and gave them posthypnotic
suggestions which, at the onset of nagging, would send
them into a deep, peaceful state of relaxation, from which
they arouse themselves only to mutter occasionally, "Yes,
dear." He calls it "Peace of Mind" hypnosis—amusing,
but nevertheless indicative of some of the imaginative uses
to which hypnotism is destined to be put in the decade
ahead. Incidentally, another recognized psychiatrist, B. J.
Hartman, also uses hypnotism for marital difficulties, but
his approach is the resolution of conflict.

Letting the imagination run full-range, it is entirely possible for hypnotism to be used to provide quasipsychedelic
experiences similar to those produced by the controversial
drug LSD and its cousins peyote and mescaline. Use of
these drugs is on the increase. Its users are in quite a different category from those of the narcotic or depressive
drugs. They are often aware experimenters rather than
obsessed addicts; they are rebels against society, seeking
to expand their conscious horizons beyond the environment around them.

A new "religion" has been formed around LSD. There
is evidence that it is becoming a social intoxicant used in
small private gatherings by people of above average means
and intelligence. "Even a common restaurant looked like
the most beautiful place in the world," one woman is
quoted as saying. Another, "It broadens the perspective I
have on myself."

These reactions and others border very closely on the
reactions of a person who has been given posthypnotic
suggestions sensitizing his senses of sight, smell, touch,
and hearing. If there is a similarity, and if the resulting
posthypnotic state produces the expanded environment experience sought by users of psychedelic drugs, then hypnotism presents a far safer means to this end.

For, although there are many for whom these hallucinogenic drugs have meant a sharpened awareness and

renewed existence, there are a certain number of casualties—suicides, mental breakdowns, and other unwanted temporary or permanent conditions. These very real dangers are valid reasons for rigid control of the psychedelic or hallucinogenic drugs.

If a prescribed state of hypnosis is considered an adequate substitute by the consciousness expanders, it would have the advantage of being completely harmless and without the slightest trace of aftereffects. The procedure would be for the person desiring this experience to pay one or two visits to the hypnologist for proper prehypnosis discussion and tests and a single induction and posthypnotic suggestion session. The subject would be instructed on how to turn on the desired effects later, and how to turn them off. It would be as simple as raising his left arm above his head, or repeating a word of command to himself, or both.

The experience itself might be described as one in which the world becomes intense. Sounds become distinct, sights more sparkling and colorful. One's mind seems more aware of things that have been taken for granted. Unimportant objects, like a pencil, or a glass of water, are seen as if for the first time. This is all part of the psychedelic experience. Now this is not exactly the kind of access to the vast, intricate, and awesome reaches of the mind claimed by the users of the "mind-manifesting" psychedelic drugs. Nor is it productive necessarily in this elementary stage of the vivid dreamlike visions with symbolic and mythologic content claimed for LSD. But it remains for those who are involved in this type of experimentation to utilize the hypnotism approach and make a comparison. Certainly there is some hope that a dangerous usage can be altered to a safe usage without loss of fulfillment.

Prehypnosis Training for Eventualities

Medicine has its preventive inoculations. Hypnotism has its prehypnosis training. A person can prepare himself now to cope with problems later through hypnotism. He has access to a hypnologist now. He may not have later. So he can prepare himself for dental surgery, for alleviation of pain due to illness, for habit control, even for accelerated learning.

Prehypnosis training involves the steps leading to attaining a good state of hypnosis—interview, susceptibility testing, induction, posthypnotic suggestion. In this case, where no particular symptom, habit, or ability is yet involved, the posthypnotic suggestion is directed by the hypnologist toward instantaneous attainment of the same state on the subject's own command at some future time.

Informed about this prehypnosis training, a dental surgeon can proceed with the extraction without anesthesia within five seconds. A music teacher can condense five lessons into one. A period of great stress, emotion, or tension can be transformed into one of greater tranquility in which reason can best operate.

Persons so prepared become in effect self-hypnotists. They can reinforce the hypnologist's suggestions from time to time so as to perpetuate the power of his hypnosis-producing suggestions. They can also give themselves suggestions in hypnosis which will help them in a variety of problems covered in previous chapters.

The application extends to serious physical illness. The physician, knowing that prehypnosis training has been given the patient even years previously, can invoke the hypnotic state for symptom control or pain relief even in cases where the conditions would make it difficult to attain hypnosis starting from scratch.

There are instances where patients in severe pain despite sedation are rendered poor hypnosis subjects because of their condition. Even the sedation itself can interfere with the hypnotic process.

The potential advantages of prehypnosis training are unlimited. There is no doubt that the complexities of twenty-first-century life and their by-products in mental and physical disorder will necessitate a new kind of "miracle" approach. Hypnosis may be it.

Possibilities for Vocational Use

Yogis have performed apparently superhuman feats for centuries. Their psychological attitude and concentration is certainly a form of self-hypnosis. Applying their success to Western directions, there is a future for hypnotism in the improvement of everyday physical skills needed by the worker and wage earner.

Whether the skills of the hypnologist can ever be made as universally available as would be needed for such popular use is the crucial question. At present these skills are in such short supply that even critical needs cannot be met. Hopefully, in the years ahead, education will rise to meet this challenge and create an increasing flow of skilled technicians in the field of hypnology.

If this comes about, education itself can benefit, for hypnologists can be used by educators to improve the success of their own processes. This can happen not only in the academic areas but in the vocational workshops where skills are acquired by youngsters who will use them to earn their livelihood.

These skills can be acquired more quickly with hypnotic preparation. They can be acquired to a higher degree with hypnotic preparation. And they can be applied more accurately with hypnotic preparation. The machinist makes his readings with a keener eye. The neophyte woodworker cuts and shapes like an old-timer. Both have a keener sense of touch and a greater overall awareness as they use their special tools and check their instruments.

Subjects under hypnosis can perform the most complex processes of learning, problem solving, and computation. They can surpass in hypnosis their "normal" capacities. Actually their performance under hypnosis is normal. It is the freeing of their normal ability to perform closer to top capacity. This is partially the reason for better occupational skill also made possible through hypnotism. A conscious feeling of limitation is largely removed as an inhibiting factor. The subject is free to perform at his true level.

The advantages to an expanding economic society are immense. A coalition of management and labor in implementing a program of skill development through hypnosis can yield better products, greater profits, higher pay, more enjoyable working conditions.

Hypnosis in Crime Detection

We have seen how hypnoanalysis has permitted the psychotherapist to get at truths buried in the innermost recesses of the mind and covered over with layer on layer of protective attitudes and beliefs. The lie detector uses chemical changes that take place in the human body when a conscious lie is present. But the fallibility of the lie detector becomes apparent when the lie is not conscious. No measured chemical changes take place, because the lie is believed as the truth by the subject himself.

Hypnosis is a more accurate lie detector. A skilled hypnologist working with a willing subject can get at the truth and know when he has arrived. The subject need not know the results, through the suggestion of posthypnotic amnesia, or he may be permitted to remember the fact dredged up from his subconscious mind.

The suspect can be made to act out the crime if he is the criminal. The dramatization can, in fact, take place from the initial preparation right through to the final act and subsequent evasive or cover-up actions. Police can be taken to where the loot is hidden or where the weapon has been disposed of. The body can be located in the case of a corpseless murder, accomplices can be identified, and previous crimes brought to light. There can be no doubt of the authenticity of these types of subconscious "confessions."

The problems of willingness on the part of the subject and acceptability as legal evidence do not seem insurmountable problems. Seemingly insurmountable at the present time, though, is the same obstacle of an educational bottleneck that is holding up the broad progress of hypnotism as a boon to society today.

Implications in Space

Since hypnotism is an effective tool in helping man to cope with his environment, its use in helping him to cope with the changed environments of space travel is a natural development and one that is already being investigated.

Several applications come to mind immediately in regard to current problems. If spacemen must maintain uncomfortable positions for long periods of time, this discomfort can be eliminated by posthypnotic suggestion. The boredom of long periods of time in space can be alleviated through time distortion, and the interplanetary months shrunk to weeks or even days.

Even metabolic processes might be slowed to make decreased use of available oxygen and water supplies. In

India, fakirs demonstrate this when they permit themselves to be buried for hours in shallow graves or coffins. Respiration is slowed to as little as five breaths per minute by suggestion, or autosuggestion in their case, and a few cubic feet of air made to last many times as long as normal.

The training period, in which suitable posthypnotic suggestions are given to condition for comfort, time distortion, and metabolism slow-up, can also be used to increase the realism of simulated flight techniques. The astronaut can be told in hypnosis that the test about to be made is real, and when the hypnosis is terminated, the simulated flight conditions will be accepted more closely as the real thing emotionally and physiologically.

Although drugs can be used to induce relaxation and other effects conducive to the space environment, they are not subject to the control possible with hypnosis, and their side effects on the subject can interfere with top-level performance and efficiency. On the other hand, hypnotism not only has no such side effects but can also be used to induce efficiency and the keener awareness required at times of takeoff, docking, descent, and other space maneuvers.

There is no doubt that as the space program advances, it will find new uses for hypnotism based on new requirements demanded of man and his phenomenal mind.

New Health Frontiers of Hypnosis

Whenever a cure of an organic disease through the use of hypnotic suggestion is reported in medical journals, it sounds so preposterous to medical men that they are inclined to discredit the original diagnosis rather than to believe the possibility of cure. How can Parkinson's disease be cured by suggestion! How can organic paralysis be cured by suggestion! How can lead poisoning be cured by suggestion!

It is still hard for men of science to believe that suggestion can cause physiological change in the body. It still smacks of the occult and paranormal to many doctors, as it does to a segment of the public. Even the creation of blisters by suggestion, demonstrated under controlled conditions and observed by skeptical physicians, is controversial despite positive results in test after test.

It is little wonder that physicians find it difficult to understand how suggestions to a patient can result in deadly germs giving up the ghost, or apparently inoperative nerve tissue coming to life. It seems preposterous to a scientific mind.

Yet, the link that will satisfy their scientific mind is close by, and if they had the same spirit of inquiry and openmindedness that paved the way for the discovery and acceptance of the very medical principles with which they work, they would waste no time denying and debating but instead would examine the known effects of suggestion on certain life processes.

The body has many ways in which it combats disease. White blood corpuscles, bloodstream antibodies, and various gland secretions are known to throw off disease and build immunity. Damage to the body triggers increased cellular growth that repairs the flesh and the bones.

But suggestion can affect the glands, the heart, and other organs of the body, especially those that can be affected by emotions, and they are many. In fact, emotion and suggestion work in the same way to affect the physical functioning of the body. What the mind brings on in the almost endless list of psychosomatic diseases, suggestion can halt.

The link still to be discovered is just how this comes about. Just how does the mind know to send less acid to the stomach, once confidence has replaced acid-producing worry through suggestion? If this link could be studied, it might be learned that even further bodily effects could be demonstrated by suggestion. An idea of health has been known to bring health. A fear of illness has been known to bring illness.

Even such a statement as "He makes me sick" has brought nausea and stomach upset. "It irritates me" or "It gets under my skin" can cause skin irritations. A "pain in the neck" brings a pain in the neck, and "Oh, my aching back" manifests the idea with great fidelity. Call it accidental hypnosis, but do not call its effects accidental. Ideas bring out physical changes in the body through the emotions.

These physical changes can conceivably include the production of white blood corpuscles to fight disease, the production of new cells to rebuild devitalized tissue, and the production of youth-producing fluids and secretions. There certainly deserves to be research on these possibilities.

Cancer is believed by many to be a purposeless cell growth caused when the purpose of the cells has been frustrated by repeated injury or irritation. It is conceivable that if a subject's own sense of frustration could be corrected by suggestion, so might his cells—possibly with some emotional linkage utilized.

Education and research go hand in hand. Hypnotism cries for both.

The Hypnologist of Tomorrow

The call is clear. Education will in the years ahead embrace hypnotism within its curricula. Criteria will be set up for accreditation of the clinical hypnologist, perhaps even for the social hypnologist, industrial hypnologist, and others.

The hypnologist will be a skilled practitioner. He will understand the portent of his power and will become the permissive catalyst in suggestive therapy rather than the subjugator of will. Even in matters producing anesthesia, he will permit the subject pain if the subject subconsciously needs it in his personality makeup or problems. He will seek cooperative rather than forced action. He will donate his services for some portion of the week to clinical research and experimentation conducted with physicians and psychiatrists.

The hypnologist of tomorrow will be a far cry from Mesmer, Braid, and Freud. He will be respected by his contemporaries in the medical world and looked to for uninterrupted contributions to the expanding knowledge of man about himself.

As man evolves he becomes what would earlier have been considered superman. Were man as he is today to appear to prehistoric man, he would be looked on as a god. Were we to be able to see the man of tomorrow we too would consider what we saw to be some kind of superhuman.

He might be many times more dexterous, more mentally proficient, more strongly constituted. He might have a greater life expectancy. He might even have developed mental abilities, sensory and extrasensory perceptions beyond conception today.

If these are possibilities, then it is an even greater possibility that hypnotism, yesterday's outcast handmaiden of mysticism, will become the master key to man's tomorrow.